WOR
METRO
SYSTEMS

Paul Garbutt

Capital Transport

First published 1989
Second edition 1997

ISBN 1 85414 191 0

Published by Capital Transport Publishing
38 Long Elmes, Harrow Weald, Middlesex

Printed by CS Graphics, Singapore

Contents

Introduction

Metros now represent one of the main growth sectors of the railway industry throughout the world. In a worldwide poll of capital expenditure by metro and other rapid transit undertakings, carried out by the 'International Railway Journal' in a recent year, a total capital outlay approaching US$12,000 million was recorded – most of it on improvements and extensions of existing operational systems, but including an impressive expenditure on new systems at the planning or construction stage.

Continuing growth of cities and of car ownership and use will, unless artificially restrained, make new metro development virtually inevitable, despite the daunting cost levels now involved. The provision of new urban highways as an alternative to building metro and rapid transit systems can prove even more costly, and certainly more wasteful of priceless city space and more damaging to the environment.

On the other hand, in a few of the great cities of the western world with long-established metro systems, the incentive to build further metro lines has tended to diminish in recent years. This is because of the decline and depopulation of the older inner suburbs and the growth of new outer suburbs and satellite towns, which are usually better served by outer suburban services of the kind normally provided by main-line railways. In such cities, further metro development is likely to be limited to strengthening the 'hub' of the system in the central area and forging links with particular traffic objectives such as airports.

For the many cities with rapidly increasing populations which are considering mass transit metro systems as a solution to their worsening in-town traffic problems, there are numerous pitfalls. For example, the city planners may be attracted to some apparently modern and non-conventional type of system, only to find when it is installed that it has inherent limitations and

4

that they are bound to a few restricted sources of supply. Again, unaware of the bitter experience of the older metro networks, they may adopt a system layout with in-built operating problems which no amount of remedial expenditure later will ever fully cure. Or they may opt for a degree of sophistication in the operating equipment which goes beyond what they need and can properly afford, and which may cause more problems than it solves. Before they commit themselves on any of these issues, the city authorities concerned would do well to seek the impartial advice of undertakings – preferably without commercial connections – which have been through the mill themselves and can recommend from experience not only what should be done, but also (and equally importantly) what should not be done. Nevertheless, so varied are the backgrounds against which new metropolitan railways are being built that virtually every new metro system presents some special problems and, when completed, adds something, however small, to the sum total of urban public transport knowledge throughout the world.

Special mention must be made of light rapid transit lines, which have lower costs – but also lower standards – than full metro lines. Such light rail systems, which have proliferated in recent years, may well prove adequate for small cities, or for internal transport within individual suburbs of larger cities

In the ultimate, advances in telecommunications technology make it less necessary for business activities to be concentrated in great cities, and this could remove some – though not all – of the justification for the building of new urban passenger railway systems. In the meantime, while most city populations grow apace and street congestion worsens, more and more civic authorities will be taking the decision to introduce some form of metro, costly though it may be, to stop their cities from grinding to a catastrophic halt.

Chapter 1

The Rise of Metros

Metropolitan railways, designed to carry large numbers of city dwellers, workers and visitors, originated in London early in the second half of the nineteenth century. As a result of the Industrial Revolution and Britain's position as the hub of a vast mercantile empire, London had become the largest city in the world, and its central thoroughfares were jammed with horse-drawn cabs, coaches and drays, and thronged with pedestrians. Suburban railways already existed to carry people to and from the central zone, but a new kind of railway was needed to distribute them within the city itself. Thanks largely to the persistence of a lawyer, Charles Pearson – who may justly be called the father of urban rail transit – a 6km (3¾ mile) underground railway was opened between Paddington and Farringdon in 1863. Other sub-surface lines followed and by the 1880s there was a substantial system in and around central London. These lines, which were operated by steam locomotives, were built in cuttings which were then roofed over for much of their length, leaving open sections at intervals to let the fumes escape. They were eventually electrified in the early 1900s.

New York was not far behind London in building a network of rapid transit rail lines, the first of which was in operation along 9th Avenue by 1870. These early New York lines were, however, all carried on elevated structures over the streets and, with their heavy iron framework and steam motive power, were a depressing, noisy and dirty addition to downtown New York. They were electrified at the turn of the century and were eventually superseded by the 'Subway', as New York's underground railway network is known.

Opposite – Building London's Metropolitan Railway at Praed Street in the early 1860s. All of the first underground railways were built by this 'cut and cover' method, as are some modern ones. *LT Museum 17449*

Above – Major construction work for the original Paris Metro, opened in 1900. *RATP*

Between 1890 and the outbreak of the First World War in 1914, there was another big wave of metro railway construction in cities around the world. New underground lines in London, criss-crossing the central area, were not built by the earlier 'cut-and-cover' method, but were bored horizontally from the bottom of deep shafts by means of tunnelling shields, known as Greathead shields after the contractor who developed and used them. Each line had twin small-diameter tube tunnels. The first line of this kind – again a world 'first' – was opened between Stockwell and the City of London, a distance of 4km (2½ miles), in 1890. The first metro transit line on the mainland of Europe was opened in Budapest in 1896, to be followed by new lines in Vienna in 1898, Paris in 1900, Berlin in 1902 and Hamburg in 1912. The first underground rapid transit line in the USA was opened in Boston in 1901; New York's first subway line began running in 1904. South America's first rapid transit line, also in tunnel, was opened in Buenos Aires in 1913. With the exception of the Vienna system, all these lines were operated electrically from the start.

The metro railway systems built before the First World War were essentially intra-city networks, complementing the suburban services of main-line railways. Apart from carrying passengers of all kinds within the central areas of cities throughout the day, most of these systems also had interchange and transfer facilities at the in-town termini of the suburban railways and were thus able to handle the concentrated peak-hour commuter traffic between those termini and the many places of work in the city centres.

A Hochbahn train at Baumwall station on the Hamburg metro in the 1920s. *HHA*

In the period between the two world wars, further cities – notably Madrid, Tokyo and Moscow – opened new metro transit systems, mostly in the form of underground railways. Existing metro networks in London, Paris and New York also grew as these great conurbations spread outwards, much of this transit development taking the form of extensions of existing lines into the inner suburbs, rather than the construction of completely new lines. The traffic nevertheless remained largely short-distance in character, little of it being filched from the suburban lines of the main-line railways.

The period since the Second World War has seen a number of phenomena, including an explosion in the world population (from 2,500 million in 1945 to over 5,500 million now), the growing concentration of population into cities (of which there are now over a hundred with more than two million inhabitants, compared with only 17 fifty years ago), and an enormous increase in the number of motor-cars and other vehicles on the highways. The result has been severe and often nightmarish road traffic congestion, particularly in the central areas of big cities in the morning and evening rush-hours.

In these conditions, more and more cities around the world have turned to public transport to take passengers out of their cars and carry them more efficiently on segregated urban railways. Thus, in comparison with the 20 or so metro systems that existed before the Second World War, there are now more than 100 in operation, with more in the pipeline. Moreover, virtually all the pre-existing systems have been expanded, many with new in-town lines to help in combating central area street congestion.

One big deterrent to the growth of metro railways in recent years has been the spectacular rise in their construction, equipment and operating costs, which have made it virtually impossible to run a rapid transit system on a strictly commercial basis any more. Many government and city authorities have nevertheless been willing to subsidise rapid transit systems heavily in order to secure the social benefits that they confer on the community. These include reduced road traffic congestion (causing fewer costly delays and accidents, cutting down city pollution and avoiding massive alternative expenditure on disruptive and space-consuming highway works), as well as reduced dependence on potentially scarce and costly oil supplies.

Chicago, 1942.
A platform scene on
the 'Loop' at Adams/
Wabash. *CTA*

Up to the Second World War, almost all metro rapid transit systems were of conventional railway type, with multiple-unit trains running on 'duorail' track; a notable exception was the Wuppertal 'Schwebebahn', or suspended railway, in Germany. Systems developed or expanded since the end of the war have, however, included some with unusual or advanced features, such as expanded segmental tunnel linings in London and elsewhere; automatic train operation and control (culminating in totally unmanned trains in Lille, Kobe and elsewhere); rubber-tyred trains in Paris and other French cities, Montreal, Mexico City, Santiago (Chile) and three Japanese cities; submerged tunnel construction for water crossings in San Francisco, Rotterdam and Stockholm; and elevated monorail construction in Tokyo, Osaka and Kitakyushu. Rapid transit lines have also taken on new roles, including the linking of airports with the city transit networks, as in London, Cleveland and Chicago, and the support of the development of new satellite towns, as in Toronto and Stockholm, where rapid transit has been planned as an integral part of each town development from the start. Yet another post-war feature relates to the phasing of metro construction, notably in Belgian and German cities, where the initial stage involves putting existing tramways into new tunnels through the city centre, and the latter stage consists of replacing the tramcars with full-size rapid transit trains and segregating the surface sections from all other traffic.

So wide is the range of urban rail systems in terms of function and design that it is very often difficult to decide whether a particular network can be properly defined as a metro rapid transit system or not. Two extreme cases may be cited: first, an outer suburban railway which penetrates the central city area for a short distance but which carries little or no short-journey traffic wholly within the central zone; and secondly, a street railway or tramway which may be partly underground or elevated but is neither signalled throughout nor fully segregated from other street traffic on its surface sections. Strictly speaking, neither of these cases should be classified as a metro.

The classic metro transit system might be defined as a high-capacity self-contained network which serves the central area and inner suburbs of a city; which carries traffic which is largely made up of intra-city journeys; which is signalled or automatically controlled throughout; which has station platforms at car floor level; and which is physically segregated from all other forms of transport but has, wherever desirable, easy passenger interchange with outer-suburban railway and local bus or tramway services.

In the chapters which follow, we consider the case for rail transit systems in the modern city, the factors involved in planning and building a metro, and the problems of the day-to-day running and maintenance of such a system when built.

Subsequent chapters set out the background history and salient features of individual metro systems throughout the world, each chapter dealing with a particular continent or group of continents.

9

Tight curves on the Lake and Wells Street intersection, Chicago. *CTA*

Chapter 2
The Case for Metros

From the standpoint of the community, the balance between public and private transport should depend on how efficiently each of them uses the limited resources available – in particular space, energy and money – and how far each meets the individual needs of the travelling public.

In the best use of space, for example, public transport is pre-eminent. Thus a single line of urban railway can carry 50,000 or more people in one direction in an hour, which is four or five times the capacity of a fast eight-lane motorway, assuming the average peak-hour car load of between one and two people. Moreover, the urban underground or elevated railway makes little or no demand on surface space, other than a very limited requirement at stations. To attempt to carry the whole commuter traffic of the older metropolitan cities such as London, Paris and New York by private car would not just be prohibitively costly and disruptive; quite simply, it would be physically impossible. About a million people enter central London during each morning peak period; 75 per cent of them do so by rail (and a further 8 per cent by bus). In New York, it has been estimated that if all the commuters entered the city by car, the whole of Manhattan below 50th Street would have to be transformed into a car park. Even in such a city as Los Angeles, dedicated more than any other to the private car and where no less than two-thirds of the central area consists of highways and parking space, metro and light rail lines are now being developed.

Now let us look at the limitations imposed by energy resources. Although a slackening in the world demand for oil and the discovery of new oil reserves have made the oil situation less critical than it appeared a few years ago, the world still needs to start planning for the post-oil age. Worldwide, the private car is a very wasteful consumer of energy resources. For every passenger-kilometre it uses about 0.9 kwh of energy, compared with only about 0.2 kwh per passenger kilometre for a city bus. Perhaps a little surprisingly, the figure for the London Underground is as much as 0.5 kwh per passenger-kilometre, because of the fairly high tare weight of the vehicles in relation to the passenger load; but unlike the private car and the bus, the electric railway does not have to carry its source of energy on the vehicle, but derives its power from a fixed generating station which can be fuelled by other means than oil.

The third great constraint on passenger transport in cities is money. Nowadays, a substantial part of the capital and operating costs of public transport is often met from national or local taxation, and the situation is often seen by the motorist as unfair, since he appears to be bearing a good deal more of the total cost of his transport than the public transport user does of his. The true picture is different. The metropolitan railway and the bus are being subsidised because they are much more efficient, in terms of resources, than the private car, and because their decline or abandonment would cost the urban community much more dearly by way of traffic congestion, wasted fuel, environmental damage and pollution. Indeed, in the inner areas of cities, the existing motorist has public transport to thank for the fact that traffic congestion is not much worse than it already is.

There are other important social reasons for giving support from public funds towards keeping up a high standard of public transport. One is that there will always be large sections of the public who do not have access to private transport – the poor, the young, the elderly and even, for much of the day, the families of the car commuters themselves. These are surely all entitled to an adequate level of personal mobility. Yet a further justification for supporting urban railway and bus facilities is their value as standby facilities when the car is out of action or when bad weather makes driving difficult or dangerous.

Urban railway construction and improvement are especially dominated by finance. New metro lines can cost anything between £20 million and £120 million per kilometre, according to the type of system and form of construction; and because the traffic carried on urban railways is usually heavily concentrated in the peak hours (so that most of the costly facilities provided to deal with the maximum peak-hour demand are wasted for the rest of the day), such lines are almost invariably run at a substantial loss. Even so, the costs of building and running a new metro line or lines can often be shown to be warranted by the scale of the resultant benefits to the community, though construction has nevertheless had to be delayed or curtailed in many cases because the capital effort involved has been beyond the national and local resources immediately available.

A further financial factor is that of efficiency. Although a metro may justify a high and sustained level of support from public funds, the subsidy should not be open-ended, and every effort must be made to secure good value for the public's money. In particular, a watch must be kept to ensure that productivity is maintained and if possible improved, although there may sometimes be cases where labour is cheap or where it is official policy to create and maintain jobs at a loss so as to reduce unemployment.

As might be expected, certain 'rules of thumb' have evolved to help in judging the point in a city's development at which a metropolitan railway system becomes desirable or necessary. Under European conditions, for example, it is generally thought that a city with an urban and suburban population of one million or more should be considered for the introduction of a metro. In typical North American conditions, a higher population figure of 1½ to 2 millions has been quoted as the minimum, and other criteria have been added including employment for at least 100,000 people in the central area, a central population density of at least 4,500 per square kilometre, and daily flows to the central area totalling at least 40,000 people in each main approach corridor.

These guidelines, though useful for a first appraisal, are by no means rigid, and there must often be cases which fall outside them. In any event, it is important that the decision to build a metro should not be taken in isolation, but within the framework of a development plan for the whole metropolitan area which brings the planning of land use into line with the balanced planning of all transport facilities and needs (railways, buses, tramways, highway construction, traffic engineering, car use restrictions, car parking, and so on).

The individual case for building a particular new urban line or network may rest on one or more of three bases, which may be defined as commercial, social and developmental. From the purely commercial standpoint, it is rarely indeed that a new metro can now be justified. The heavy construction, maintenance and operating costs, coupled with the usually highly-peaked and therefore uneconomic traffic demand, prevent all but a very few new rapid transit lines from paying their way. Among the rare 'money-spinners' in recent decades was the extension of the London Underground to Heathrow Airport; this short extension tapped a big new source of traffic, which travelled widely over the Underground network.

Under the second heading – the social case – there are often strong grounds for building new metro lines, which can avoid costly and offensive new highway construction, reduce traffic congestion, shorten journeys and relieve overloading on existing public transport services (including suburban railways and any existing metro lines, as well as buses and tramways).

Starting with the Victoria Line project in London in 1962, it has become the general practice to use 'social cost/benefit assessment' techniques to help to judge new urban metro projects. The 'benefit' side of these cost/benefit analyses is calculated from the traffic estimates for the new lines, which are themselves the result of new estimating methods developed over recent decades. Real savings in journey times and other benefits in travel conditions and opportunities caused by the new line (including, for example, the relief of road congestion and the reduction in road accidents) are translated into equivalent money values wherever possible. These money values, together with the actual money savings (for example, the cost savings on buses and cars made possible by the diversion of traffic to the new line), are then set against the project costs. The net change in revenue to public transport is also taken into account. All the money values are discounted to present values over a period of, say, fifty years.

Although it has been developed and refined over the years, the method is still less than perfect, mainly because a number of obvious benefits (including the improvement of access to shops and entertainment, the widening of employment opportunities and labour markets, and the 'standby' value of the new line) are difficult if not impossible to quantify, and because the indices of value applied to other benefits cannot be more than notional in character. Nevertheless, a high ratio of benefits to costs is accepted as a strong recommendation for building a new metro line. Cost/benefit studies have proved useful, too, in judging between alternative metro schemes.

The third basis of justification for a new metro line is the increase in property values and development prospects along the route of the line. Different people feel these benefits in different ways. The values of existing properties within the 'catchment' area of the line are enhanced. The potential for developing and redeveloping properties alongside the line is greatly increased. The metro railway authority's own operating properties, especially the stations, have great development potential – for example, by building office blocks above them. And finally, the city's property taxation revenues benefit as a result of the increase in value of all types of property along the line.

As an indication of the scale of the enhancement of property values as a result of a new metro transit facility, it was reported that Toronto's original Yonge Street subway line of 1954 set off a $10 billion property development boom, so that the extra tax revenues alone more than paid for the initial cost of the line, amounting to $67 million.

Again, in Hong Kong, the Mass Transit Railway Authority announced in 1983 that judicious property development on and over its railway sites had contributed HK$1.05 billion (nearly 20 per cent) towards the HK$5.6 billion capital cost of the initial metro line, and over HK$0.4 billion (over 10 per cent) towards the HK$3.9 billion capital cost of the extension towards the new town of Tsuen Wan. Similar contributions were forthcoming on the Island Line, which was opened later.

Studies in a number of other major cities around the world confirm that the coming of a new urban railway 'triggers off' the latent potential along its route for development of all kinds. By the same token, new metro railways may be developed as an instrument of land use policy, to support a desired pattern of urban or suburban development. Thus in Toronto, Stockholm and other cities, decentralisation has been achieved by developing major office and shopping centres around stations on new metro lines in the suburbs. In London, the movement of the port facilities downstream to Tilbury left the original 'Docklands' area derelict, and a local metro (the Docklands Light Railway) has been built as part of the plan for the commercial and residential revival of the area.

Opposite – U-Bahn train on an elevated section of the Berlin system. One railway track has more passenger capacity than all the highway lanes put together. *BVG*

Chapter 3
Planning

One of the earliest decisions that has to be taken in planning a new metro system is the particular form of railway to be adopted. The great majority of the world's urban metro and underground systems, existing and under construction, are of conventional railway type, known for ease of reference as 'duorail' or 'steel-on-steel'.

There is wide experience of the techniques of operating conventional steel-on-steel urban rail transit lines, and manufacturers in many industrialised countries are geared to the production of rolling stock, track, signalling and other equipment for them. The idea of the steel-on-steel railway is simple, in that the same small number of wheels carry, drive and guide the vehicles, the road-bed needs no special supporting structure, and the points and switches are compact and quick to operate. Altogether, therefore, there is a strong prima facie case for adopting the conventional type of rail transit system.

However, in an endeavour to reduce the noise level associated with steel-on-steel and to improve acceleration and braking performance, the French decided, after the Second World War, to develop an alternative system utilising rubber-tyred trains running on parallel beams. There are now, however, various means available to suppress noise on steel-on-steel systems, including continuous welded rail, lineside sound absorption screens and sound insulation on trains. Both Berlin and Hamburg have steel-on-steel systems which are marginally quieter than the Paris rubber-tyred railways.

The advantages of higher acceleration and braking rates claimed for the rubber-tyred vehicles, and their ability to negotiate steeper gradients, are moreover largely illusory. In the first place, acceleration and braking rates much in excess of those obtainable with steel-on-steel are unacceptable from the standpoint of passenger comfort and safety. Secondly, in a modern design of steel-wheeled vehicle, in which most if not all of the axles are motor-driven, there is rarely any difficulty in providing sufficient adhesion over the worst unavoidable gradients.

Opposite – Campo Grande – a major bus/metro interchange station on the Lisbon metro, a conventional steel-on-steel railway. *Capital Transport*

Above – A depot for rubber-tyred trains, Mexico City. *STC Metro*

The disadvantages of the rubber-tyred system are that it is costly and cumbersome in respect of track design, with a total of six beams and rails in a single track, and in respect of bogie design, with each bogie having no fewer than 12 rubber and metal wheels. The axle-load is relatively low, and this normally limits the car size to about 17–17.5m (56–57ft) long by 2.6m (8½ft) wide, the high level of heat generation can cause problems of ventilation, and there can be adhesion problems on open-air sections when the beams are wet and when snow settles on them. Also current consumption is substantially greater.

The Paris rubber-tyred system has been adopted in that city and the main French provincial cities, but only in three cities outside France, namely Montreal, Mexico City and Santiago de Chile, with mixed success. It is noteworthy that in Paris itself, only four out of the 13 urban lines use the rubber-tyred system, though the new 'Meteor' line has rubber-tyred trains. It is also noteworthy that the whole of the Regional Express System (RER) has been developed as a conventional steel-on-steel railway.

Much publicity has been given since the Second World War to monorails, of both the straddle and suspended types, and a limited number of monorail lines have been built, mostly to handle relatively low-density traffics or in exhibitions and leisure parks. Apart from Wuppertal, with its historic suspended monorail already mentioned, only two cities, Chiba and Kitakyushu in Japan, have monorails as their main segregated rail systems, and the traffic on them has been relatively light. Probably the best known monorail is the 17km (10½ mile) line linking the edge of Tokyo's inner city with the important Haneda Airport, but its peak load in recent years has been no more than 6,000 passengers in one direction in an hour. Over the years, a number of comprehensive transport studies, notably for San Francisco, Manchester and Hong Kong, have specifically rejected monorail systems because of their demonstrable disadvantages compared with the conventional duorail railway. These disadvantages can include higher capital cost, particularly on sections in tunnel and at ground level; cumbersomeness, especially in switching arrangements and bogie design; lack of operational flexibility; maintenance and inspection difficulties; and problems of passenger detrainment in emergency.

A further system has been developed in the last twenty-five years, namely the Japanese Kawasaki system installed on the rapid transit lines in Sapporo, the venue for the 1972 Olympic Winter Games. This system is akin to the Paris rubber-tyred metro system (although it uses a centre guide-beam instead of side beams), and it suffers several of the drawbacks of that system. For example, while a six-car train of conventional metro rolling stock is carried and guided by only 48 metal wheels, a Kawasaki-type train of the same length requires no fewer than 160 rubber wheels for support and guidance. Also, because of the problems posed by snow, the whole of the open-air part of the Sapporo network has had to be enclosed in a snow shed.

On the Sapporo metro, part of the line has been enclosed in a snow shed to protect the rubber-tyred system from winter weather.
Y. Sakamoto

There remain for consideration certain systems which have only comparatively recently been brought into everyday use or which are still the subject of research and development, at least so far as their possible application to urban passenger railways is concerned. These include, among others, propulsion by linear induction motors, hovertrains, high-speed passenger conveyor systems and 'minitubes'. One or two of these are promising and have been successfully adopted in pioneer projects; for example, linear induction motors are employed on two light rapid transit ('ALRT') lines in Canada – in a Toronto suburb and in Vancouver – and there is a short magnetic-levitation 'hovertrain' link at Birmingham (UK) International Airport. But for many of these novel systems, it is doubtful if the timescale of their development will enable them to be considered for heavily-loaded urban lines projected in the near future.

One factor that must be taken into account in deciding on the system to be used for a new metro is the need for reliability and ruggedness. Day in and day out, the installations and equipment of a metro railway are subjected to the most punishing treatment, and the technology employed therefore needs to be straightforward and robust. As the early days of the Bay Area Rapid Transit (BART) system in San Francisco showed, over-sophistication and the use of untried technology can prove disastrous. There may be problems, too, in maintaining high-technology equipment.

Similarly, the degree of automation to be adopted in a new metro needs to be carefully weighed. Where suitable staff would be difficult or costly to recruit, a high level of automation is clearly desirable. But where – as in many of the so-called developing countries – competent staff can be easily recruited at low wage rates, the need for extensive automation may be questionable.

Yet another factor in the choice of system is equipment supply. New metros which adopt non-conventional systems often find themselves tied to sole suppliers of equipment or, at best, a single country of supply. Metros adopting modern conventional systems and standards, on the other hand, can benefit from competitive bids for rolling stock, plant and equipment from manufacturers in virtually all the major industrial countries of the world. Research and development programmes for non-conventional systems can also be expensive.

So, in view of all the factors spelt out above, there seems little doubt that for the foreseeable future, most cities which contemplate building new metropolitan railways will adopt the conventional steel-on-steel duorail system, with manned trains.

Other important and early decisions to be made in planning a new metro concern the proportions of tunnel, surface and elevated construction, and the layout of the network. Because of the heavy cost of tunnelling, it is usual to limit underground construction as far as possible to the sections through the congested central area, bringing the line to the surface through the inner suburbs and continuing to the outer terminal in the open, sometimes on elevated structure along the median strip of major highways.

Thus, for example, of the 392 km (244 miles) of operational route of the London Underground network, only 171 km (106 miles) are actually underground, though these are mostly in the central area and carry the bulk of the traffic. Similarly, of 115 km (71 miles) of the modern Bay Area (San Francisco) Rapid Transit system, only 31 km (19 miles) are in tunnel, the remainder being divided roughly equally between surface and elevated construction. As the modern San Francisco and Vancouver systems show, elevated railways can be carried on slender piers, so that the structures need not be either inelegant or offensive in a suburban setting, avoiding the uglier features which characterised the early elevated railways in such cities as New York and Chicago.

No less than 99% of the Barcelona municipal metro is underground, two short sections rising to the surface for access to depots. A train on Line L1 approaches Mercat Nou station in September 1996.
Capital Transport

Below – Latest stock on the Boston Red Line, seen on a median strip descending from the Longfellow Bridge in September 1996.
Brian Patton

As regards the planning of routes and network layouts, certain principles have been established from long experience in the development and operation of urban and suburban railways in the major metropolitan cities of the world. Failure to observe these principles can cause persistent operating and traffic problems which can only be surmounted later – if, indeed, at all – at enormous expense.

First, in the largest cities, there is a clear distinction in traffic, operating and rolling stock requirements between the outer-suburban type of line (usually part of the main-line railway system) on the one hand, and the urban/inner suburban 'metro' type of line on the other hand. The average journey on an outer-suburban system is relatively long – generally of the order of 16–24 km (10–15 miles) – and the traffic builds up from a number of tributary branches in the inward direction in the morning peak period and is dispersed outwards again from the in-town terminus in the evening peak. The services on the individual outer branches may be comparatively infrequent, and although the combined train frequencies on the 'funnel' section at the in-town end may be high, this section is normally multiple-tracked. The outer suburban stations are not closely spaced, and because of the length of journeys, the service pattern generally provides for a proportion of 'non-stop' running. As for rolling stock performance on outer-suburban services, high maximum speed is more important than high braking and acceleration rates. Also, outer-suburban trains should have a high proportion of seating accommodation because of the journey lengths, but in view of the tidal nature of the traffic, wide automatic doors for simultaneous boarding and alighting are not essential.

The urban metro or 'rapid transit' type of line, on the other hand, performs a basically different function, namely the distribution of traffic of all kinds locally within the central area of a city, including peak-hour traffic brought in by the outer-suburban services of the main-line railways. In addition, it may deal with some short-distance commuter traffic between the inner suburbs and the centre. Metro stations are sited at frequent intervals – usually about $1/2$–$3/4$ mile ($3/4$–$1 1/4$ kilometre) – and there are often heavy simultaneous boarding and alighting movements at them. The service must be intensive, with a frequency of up to 30 or 40 trains per hour each way in the peak period on one pair of tracks. For reasons of line capacity and train loadings, all trains must normally serve all stations. The rolling stock should have a high acceleration and deceleration rate, rather than a high maximum speed, and in view of the shortness of the passengers' journeys, high standing capacity is more important than a lavish provision of seats. Wide automatic doors are essential for rapid simultaneous loading and unloading at stations.

An urban-type railway which goes out too far, or an outer-suburban railway which comes in too far, cannot wholly satisfy both the urban and outer suburban requirements at one and the same time. Admittedly the French authorities have been developing outer-suburban 'Regional Express' lines running into and through the centre of Paris, but these have only a few stations in the central area (with good interchanges to the existing urban Metro), and are not designed to carry short-distance intra-city traffic. The same may be said of British Rail's modern 'Thameslink' services through central London, and the Sydney and Melbourne suburban railways' lines crossing and circling the central zones.

There are normally extensive interchange facilities – passages, speedwalks (travolators), escalators and lifts – between an urban railway system and the main-line railways' terminal stations on the fringe of the central area. But easier passenger transfer can be provided between the outer-suburban and metro services, and congestion avoided, if the metro line intercepts the 'funnel' section of the outer-suburban system at an interchange station at a suitable point in the inner suburban belt. The interchange station should preferably be of the simple 'cross-platform' type. This has been done with great success in London; at the inner suburban station of Stratford, for example, passengers travelling to town by the long-distance suburban services of British Rail have only to cross an island platform to board Underground trains taking them on to their central area destinations; and the reverse applies in the outward direction. Similar interchange facilities between British Rail and the London Underground exist at Highbury and at Barking, and there are many stations where the London Transport authorities have provided the same form of two-direction cross-platform interchange between different lines of their own Underground system.

In planning the route layout of an urban metro system, there are a number of most important factors to be borne in mind, as follows:

1. The lines should be designed to follow the broad corridors of greatest traffic demand, actual or potential. These are usually radial and often (but not always) correspond to the alignments of major roads. Two radial metro routes are normally combined into a single cross-city line, so as to balance the traffic across the central area and rationalise the operation.

2. Each line should, if at all possible, be self-contained operationally. The interworking of services between lines causes major complications. For example, the joint use of sections of track limits the frequency of the individual services, and delays on one service are transmitted to others. Independently operated lines are therefore best, but easy passenger interchange should be provided between them. The metropolitan railways of Paris and Moscow have no interworking of trains between lines. In London, there is a considerable amount of complex interworking between the older Underground lines; but London Transport has profited by the pioneering errors made by its predecessors, and all its later lines – including the post-war Victoria and Jubilee lines – are self-contained. The New York Subway also has much interworking of services, using flying junctions to avoid crossing movements of trains on the flat.

3. If branches are planned, they should be strictly limited in number, preferably to only two at each end of a line. Too many branches cause great operational difficulty in bringing trains from different points together over a succession of junctions to produce a regular high-frequency service on the trunk section through the central area. Train frequency on the individual branches is limited, and for this reason the junction point should not be sited too close in to the centre. Also, branches should be laid out to produce roughly equal traffics on each; otherwise an uneven service has to be projected over the more heavily loaded branch, giving rise to uneven train loads and delays. Much the same factors apply in deciding where to site intermediate reversing points on the outer sections of line which do not have branches.

4. For operational reasons, stations should be as evenly spaced as possible, after allowing for the locations of the major traffic objectives to be served. In fact, the correct spacing and siting of stations can be quite a complex problem. It must be borne in mind that a metro passenger's journey includes the walk or ride to and from the metro station at each end of the train trip. Closely spaced stations shorten these walks, but they increase the number of train stops, and so lengthen the time spent in the train itself. The ideal station spacing is one which balances these two contrary factors so that the average door-to-door journey takes as little time as possible. In practice, of course, the presence of important traffic objectives exerts an overriding influence. Fairly close spacing of stations is usually needed in the central areas of cities, where the proportion of passengers leaving and boarding the trains is high in comparison with those going through. Close spacing also avoids an over-concentration of traffic at a single station, which may otherwise become a bottleneck, causing disturbance to the service and even impairing the capacity of the whole line. On the other hand, where the number of passengers who will use the station is small compared with the through traffic – for example, at the fringes of the central area – stations can be more widely spaced. Where stations are in shallow tunnel and the platforms are therefore quickly and easily accessible from the street, stations may be very closely spaced so as to tempt the ultra-short-distance passenger on to the metro. In Paris, for example, where there is a close mesh of shallow metro lines across the central area of the city, the average distance between the urban metro stations is little more than $\frac{1}{2}$ km (about $\frac{1}{3}$ mile), and many Parisians making very short journeys will 'hop on the Metro' in much the same way as their London counterparts 'hop on a bus'.

5. Circular railways are generally unsatisfactory, from both the operational and traffic standpoints, and it is noteworthy that of the many new rapid transit systems developed since the Second World War, relatively few include a circular line. However, Moscow did add a self contained loop line to its pre-existing system, to link together a number of main-line rail termini. The elaborate Melbourne Underground Railway Loop, the first part of which was opened in 1981, was designed largely to balance the suburban train services around that city and relieve the congested Flinders Street station, rather than as a circular metro service per se. The Circle Line of the London Underground, opened in 1884, has the justification, on traffic grounds, of linking almost all the many main-line railway termini fringing London's central area; but it illustrates many of the lasting operational disadvantages of this type of layout. Through train services coming from other Underground lines, mostly over flat junctions, on to sections of the Circle produce a rigid and complex service pattern which is most difficult to maintain. Delays may be transmitted from and through the Circle operation to many other parts of the network, and a limited frequency is imposed on the circular service itself, which has to be booked to lose time at stations where this does not block other interworked services. By their peripheral nature, circular lines tend to give round-about rather than direct passenger connections, and they rarely attract enough optional traffic to make a worthwhile contribution to their capital charges and operating costs. There are a few old circular urban railways in other great cities besides London (for example, Glasgow), but it is doubtful if they would be planned afresh in the same form today. Only in those cases where the circle is physically segregated has operation been reasonably satisfactory, and even then most of the passenger connections offered are unduly circuitous.

6. If possible, metro rolling stock depots should be located where they will involve the minimum amount of empty train movement. However, this policy is often thwarted by the difficulty and cost of acquiring sufficient land for the purpose towards the central areas of cities. For these reasons, depots often have to be sited towards the outer ends of radial metro lines.

With all the factors and precepts set out above in mind, a start can now be made with the long process which will culminate in the opening of a new metro. The first step is to draw up a series of alternative route alignments along each major traffic corridor, linking together the important centres which generate, or are expected to generate, a high level of passenger movement. This task is made easier if an effective travel survey has been carried out to establish the travel 'desire lines' – the actual or latent demand for travel between every pair of district centres in and immediately around the city.

Inside a modern metro maintenance depot – Mexico City. *STC Metro*

Using such information as already exists about the physical characteristics of each corridor, the alternative alignments are now compared with each other in general terms, taking into account their respective constructional problems and other factors such as major differences in the probable order of cost, accessibility to passengers, environmental impact and the amount of physical and social disturbance likely to be caused in providing the 'right of way'. After a careful evaluation, the most suitable metro alignment for each corridor to be served is carried forward to the next stage.

For these selected alternatives, work can now be put in hand on a firmer definition of the horizontal and vertical alignments, and for this purpose a number of standards have to be fixed, including particularly the maximum gradient and minimum radius of curve to be accepted. It is at this stage that the broad decisions will be taken on how much of the line shall be at surface level, how much elevated and how much underground – and in the last case (where a knowledge of ground conditions is most important), on the form of tunnelling and the economic size of tunnel.

It is at this stage, too, that the design of the stations is developed on broad lines, and their positions on the alignment are more firmly fixed. Likewise, rolling stock depot sites must be specified and their general shape and size established.

All these data now provide an outline plan for the new metro line or network on which a tentative assessment (the initial 'feasibility study') of the project can be based. An important part of this assessment is the estimation of the traffic effects of the scheme, and this can prove a difficult task; mathematical modelling techniques have been developed over the years for this purpose, but they can have a wide margin of error and should be regarded as providing a guide rather than a close estimate. It is an interesting fact that when the Victoria Line of the London Underground was being developed in the 1960s, a laborious station-by-station 'manual' assessment of the traffic by transport planners with a detailed knowledge of the local conditions proved, in the event, to be a good deal more accurate than the results of two separate computer model exercises which were subsequently carried out.

The traffic assessment is usually done on an annual or a 'standard working day' basis, and has to be refined down to show the expected maximum peak period (normally 20-minute) loadings on each section of line in each direction. From this can be worked out the amount of peak passenger capacity that is required in the trains, and this in turn enables decisions to be made on the dimensions, seating layout, door provision, performance and operating characteristics of the rolling stock, the number of cars per train and the maximum train frequency required. These data, coupled with the calculated total time to be taken by a train for a complete round trip on the line (including the standing or 'layover' time at each terminal), give the figures of the maximum number of trains and cars that will be in service on the line at any one time. With the addition of a percentage of spare units to cover repair and overhaul requirements (usually under 10 per cent on a line with standardised train units), the total size of the required rolling stock fleet can now be established. From all this there is a feed-back in respect of platform lengths, the size of the rolling stock depots, and so on.

The information is now available to complete the initial feasibility study of the whole project, covering the broadly estimated costs of acquiring the right of way and of building, equipping and operating the line or lines, together with the expected financial results, a comparison of benefits and costs, and an assessment of the impact on the social and fiscal development of the city, both short-term and long-term. The study must, among other things, take account of the expected effect of the project on existing public transport services; for example, as part of the overall transport policy for the city, it may be decided to switch many bus routes from radial corridors to serve instead as feeders to stations on the new metro system.

The findings of the initial feasibility study, if promising, may be used to obtain from the city or central government the authority and funds needed to carry out the next stage of the project, namely the more detailed survey and design work, which is the subject of the next chapter.

As most cities which are thinking of building their first metro lines have insufficient expertise to do so unaided, they usually have recourse to the services of specialist firms and groups of transport and engineering consultants, who are able to mastermind a project right through from the first feasibility study to the supervision of the construction and the inspection of the equipment. There are now many such specialist consulting firms and consortia, including some which are subsidiaries of – or associated with – the older and larger city public transport undertakings. From their long experience, embracing failures as well as successes, these undertakings are well qualified to advise on how and how not to go about creating a new metro.

So far has the organisation of metro development come in recent decades that it is not unusual nowadays for the specialist consultants to join 'ad hoc' consortia of engineering contractors, train and equipment suppliers, finance houses and others to bid for complete 'turnkey' schemes for the construction and equipment of new metros, and even in some cases for the subsequent operation and maintenance of the new lines to prescribed levels of service and subsidy.

Layout at Piccadilly Circus station in London. *LT Museum*

Chapter 4
Design

The design of the structures, equipment and rolling stock of a metro is a complex task involving many disciplines. It is therefore necessary to fix general standards and codes of practice, produce typical layouts for use throughout the network, and establish the relationship between different elements of the system. The last of these points can be illustrated by the type of braking adopted on trains. Regenerative braking turns braking energy into electrical energy which is fed back into the current supply system for use by trains accelerating on other parts of the network. If regenerative braking is not used, there is merit in including accelerating and decelerating ramps (the so-called 'hump' profile, as described later) in the gradient profile of the line.

The first task in the detailed design stage is to establish a firm alignment for the planned metro route or routes. For this a series of topographical surveys has to be carried out along each route, so that maps can be drawn which are accurate enough to allow precise fixing of the route and detailed design, and for control of the actual construction. It is usual to employ aerial photography for these surveys, using stereo pictures, and a typical scale for the mapping is 1/500. Secondary survey stations are also set up close to the route alignment, so as to pick up details (such as pedestrian underpasses) not shown by the aerial survey and to pinpoint any potential conflict between the metro and other new developments.

In addition to the alignment proper, it is necessary to establish a corridor along the line of route to protect it against encroachment by other new works before the metro construction can begin. This protection is given by legal powers granted to the metro authority, as explained in a later chapter. Within the corridor boundaries, areas must be earmarked for the temporary working sites needed during the construction period, and for the permanent sites required for metro structures such as stations, tunnel ventilation shafts, and the piers of elevated sections of line. To minimise expenditure, the corridor should be no wider than is absolutely necessary.

In the earlier planning stages, general geological information available from previous borings and deep excavations on the route would have been used to determine the best tunnel levels and tunnelling methods to be employed on the underground sections of route, the type of foundations needed on the elevated sections, and the preliminary design of earthworks. For detailed design, however, a thorough soil investigation must be carried out along the route corridor to identify the strata and water table, and to classify the ground from borehole samples. This information is needed to refine the gradient profile, evaluate construction methods and make cost estimates. In some parts of the world, it is also necessary to consider the risk of earthquakes; thus, for example, in Tokyo and other Japanese cities, and in North and South American cities such as San Francisco and Caracas which are in earthquake zones, metro structures have to be designed to stand up to earthquake pressures.

It is also essential to establish exactly where services such as sewers, water and gas mains, and telephone and electrical cables run. The managements of these utilities can normally provide this information, which is then plotted on the metro survey maps. Deep-level tube lines are unlikely to disturb utilities other than deep sewers. On the other hand, utilities which run along or across sections of the metro which are elevated, at surface level, or in cut-and-cover tunnel may be seriously affected by the metro works, and it is often necessary to dig trial holes to locate the precise positions of mains and sewers, so that any diversions needed can be properly planned. Trial holes may also have to be dug to fix the exact positions of building foundations and basements along the metro route.

Information is also needed on air temperature and humidity (to decide on whether the metro needs to be air-conditioned or not), and on the rainfall (to decide on drainage requirements and any special measures to prevent flooding of the metro at times of heavy rain). For example, in Calcutta, which is subject to heavy monsoon flooding, protective 'bunds' were built around openings of the new underground line (although these proved less than effective when the first section was inundated shortly before its planned opening in 1984). Measures against vibration and noise must also be incorporated in the design; as long ago as the 1860s, when the first section of London's District Line was being built through Parliament Square, the tunnel walls were made thicker to prevent damage to the matchless fabric of Westminster Abbey – then already five centuries old. A hundred years later, in straightening out the Metropolitan Line under London's new Barbican Music and Arts Centre, a special form of cushioned invert was introduced in the new 'covered way' to minimise vibration and noise. And in Hong Kong, the metro authorities completely enclosed one elevated section of line to reduce the noise of trains in a crowded housing estate.

Deep-level tunnelling in an urban area usually causes only limited interference with the life of the community, but the impact of cut-and-cover and elevated construction can be considerable. To minimise this impact, a study of road traffic and pedestrian movements in the vicinity of the metro route must be carried out, so that in collaboration with the highway authorities, traffic diversions can be planned and traffic to and from the metro working sites arranged so as to maintain the essential movements of vehicles and pedestrians, and access to buildings along the route.

On page 16 we showed an enclosed elevated section of metro to protect the line against snow. This example, in Hong Kong, was built to prevent nearby flat dwellers suffering from train noise. *MTRC*

The complete operational layout for the line or lines must also be resolved. This involves not only fixing the track and platform layouts at the terminals, but also designing flyover layouts at branch junctions (to avoid tracks crossing at the same level and so giving rise to conflicting train movements), contriving the interlacing of tracks to make 'cross-platform' passenger transfer possible at suitable interchange stations, and introducing a humped gradient profile at stations (to assist acceleration and braking) if desired. On this last point, it is of interest that the earliest section of metro railway to incorporate these accelerating and decelerating 'humps' at stations was the Central Line of the London Underground, opened between Shepherd's Bush and Bank stations in 1900; on this line, the up and down gradients are 1.66 and 3.33 per cent respectively. Besides helping trains to stop and start quickly, this humped profile also saved current, but there proved to be one drawback; if a train was brought to a stop at a home signal on the ramped approach to a station, it would take that much longer to start up again against the sharp gradient when the signal cleared. So a variation of the hump profile was later devised which provided for a short 3.33 per cent down gradient out of a station, followed at once by a gradual rise to the next station; this is known as a 'sawtooth' profile, and an adaptation of it was used wherever possible on London's Victoria Line in the 1960s, although the scope for it there was unfortunately limited. However, London's Jubilee Line extension stations have a humped profile.

It is vital, in this design stage, to consider also all the safety and emergency features that will be required, particularly in the underground sections of the new metro. Provision must be made, for example, to detrain large numbers of passengers in safety in the event of a serious breakdown or accident, and walk them along the tunnels to adjacent stations. In double-track tunnels, this presents no serious problems; but in single-track tunnels, it may be thought necessary to incorporate a narrow 'catwalk', at the level of the car floors, on one side of the line throughout its length, and this provision naturally adds to the dimensions – and therefore to the cost – of the tunnels.

Again, the design of the line must provide for some strategically placed emergency crossovers between the running tracks to permit trains to by-pass the site of a breakdown or – more usually – to reverse on either side of it. Such crossovers must be located so as to enable the curtailed service to reach a station where there are reasonable facilities to disperse the passengers. But there should not be too many emergency crossovers of this kind, and there must be clear and well-rehearsed arrangements for their use; otherwise there may be confusion at the very time when disciplined emergency operation is essential.

Fire is a particular risk on underground lines, and care must be taken in design, and in the materials used, to reduce the fire hazard to a minimum, and to provide clear and tested escape routes for passengers threatened by fire, or by terrorist action such as the serin gas attacks which killed twelve people and injured over 5,500 more on the Tokyo subway in March 1995. One factor in combating fire and terrorism on metros is uncluttered design, leaving no recesses where flammable material can accumulate or dangerous devices can be concealed.

Something has already been said in the preceding chapter about the spacing of stations, their general layout, and their location on the projected metro route or routes. Now, at the more detailed design stage, more accurate plans must be developed for every station. In the first place, it is important that the stations should be located at exactly the right place in relation to the surrounding street layouts and the centres of business and activity which they are intended to tap. Even when the station access points are only a hundred metres away from the traffic centre served, a station may not reach its full traffic potential. Sometimes there are overriding engineering reasons why a station may have to be located a short distance away from its traffic objective; in such cases, the position may be at least partially retrieved if a shop-lined arcade can be installed between the station concourse and a well-signed entrance/exit portal or stairwell right at the traffic centre.

Every station consists of a number of basic elements which include access from and to the streets, a concourse and ticketing area, platform areas where boarding and alighting takes place, passages, stairs, escalators and lifts for passenger movement within the station, the track layout, and station staff facilities. Stations may be classified in various ways – deep-level, shallow, surface or elevated – or into terminal, intermediate, reversing, interchange or through stations. When there is a surface station building, access to the ticketing area may be simply by portals or passages straight off the pavement; in the central areas of cities, however, where booking halls are generally below street level and sometimes linked with the public pedestrian underpass system, access to them is gained by stairwells from the pavement or through buildings, and sometimes by pedestrian ramps as well. There can be no ideal shape of metro station ticket hall suitable to all situations; but subject to overriding engineering factors, the layout should give direct and orderly passenger flows past the ticket offices or ticket machines to the ticket barriers, with the minimum of conflicting movements. The choice of a wall or free-standing booth type of ticket office, and the location of the entrances, machines, kiosks and barrier gates, can be made to serve this objective, and where ticket queues form, they must not be allowed to obstruct the movement of pre-booked passengers. The ticket barriers lie between the booking hall and the stairs or escalators leading to the platforms, and may be manned or automatic (i.e. operated by coins, tokens, or encoded tickets), according to the fares system adopted. In deep-level 'tube' stations (and sometimes in elevated stations), the vertical link to and from the platforms is provided by lifts or escalators, and occasionally by both. Wherever possible, escalators or lifts are arranged to run from street level to platform level, but this is of course ruled out where the booking office and concourse are at an intermediate level, or where structural or site restrictions exist.

Escalators are preferred to lifts on most modern metros because of their relatively high capacity (up to 10,000 people per machine per hour, at the optimum speed of about 45 metres per minute) and continuous operation, but lifts may be more economical at deep-level tube stations with fairly light traffic, where two flights of escalators with an intermediate landing would otherwise be necessary. An example is Hampstead station on the London Underground, which has platforms 55m (181ft) below the surface and is served by high-speed lifts. Of course, all lift-served stations must be provided with emergency stairs, which are often in the form of a spiral round the lift shaft. Deep level stations in St Petersburg and Moscow are served by long escalators which can add up to five minutes to the exit time after leaving the train.

Multi-level metro station in Montreal, showing escalator interchange. *STCUM*

At surface or shallow sub-surface stations, all vertical movement is normally by stairs, but there are some exceptions where it has been thought worthwhile to fit escalators. In some stations, for example where an interchange between lines involves an extensive walk, travolators (moving walkways) may be installed in long passages.

On some of the more modern metro lines, such as those in Hong Kong, the authorities concerned have endeavoured to produce a standard 'box' structure for the stations, with the minimum amount of local variation from the standard. The box is usually located under a major city thoroughfare, and contains a mezzanine level forming the booking area and passenger concourse, linked by stairwells up to strategic points on the street pavements and by further stairways or escalators

The impressive Dhoby Ghaut metro station in Singapore. *LTA, Singapore*

down to the platforms at the bottom level. This concept was carried further on the underground sections of the State Street and Congress lines of the Chicago Transit system, opened in 1943 and 1951 respectively. In the downtown area, the State Street line has a continuous centre 'island' platform over 1km (some 3,500ft) long and 6.7m (22ft) wide. Although there are eight mezzanine-level stations connected to the platform, there are only three actual train stopping points along each side of it. Similarly, on the Congress line under Milwaukee Avenue, there is a continuous island platform over 3/4km (some 2,500ft) long with six mezzanine stations connected to it. The idea behind this unique layout was evidently to maximise the number of street access points in relation to the actual number of train stopping points.

In the internal design of stations, it is important to ensure that passages and stairs (including not only those linking the concourse with the street and platforms, but also those linking the platforms of different lines at interchange stations which do not have cross-platform transfer) shall have adequate capacity to cope with the passenger flows expected at the height of the peak traffic periods. Operational research carried out in London and Paris some time ago established approximate indices of capacity for passages and stairs, namely 90 persons a minute per metre width (about 27 per foot width) in level passages, 60 per metre width (about 19 per foot width) on upward stairs, and nearly 70 per metre width (about 21 per foot width) on downward stairs.

If passages, stairs or escalators to and from platforms at different stations are all in the same relative position to the trains, one or two cars of each train will always be more heavily loaded than the rest. For more even loading of the cars, platform entrances and exits should be differently located at different stations.

Many metro systems worldwide have employed unique decorative schemes for particular stations. This has been uncommon in the USA but the recently-opened metro in Los Angeles includes neon light designs at Pershing Square station and murals at MacArthur Park. *Capital Transport*

Distinctive logos at metro station entrances are particularly important in city centres where subway stairs could otherwise easily be missed. *Capital Transport*

Metro stations need to incorporate a recognisable 'house style' so that passengers can identify a metro building station entrance, concourse or platform on sight; but at the same time, the design of stations should be sensitive to their surroundings, and should where possible include some concession to the architectural character and style of the neighbourhood in which they are set.

There are quite wide variations in the architecture and decor of the metro stations of different cities and different periods. The earliest metro stations, on the original sections of the London Underground in the mid-Victorian era, were heavy brick structures, solid but often imposing. They were followed in the late Victorian and Edwardian period by 'tube' stations with rather drab exterior tiling, but more distinctive and attractive platform tiling. The inter-war period was the heyday of London Underground station design, when architect Charles Holden produced a series of new stations which were at once functional, elegant and impressive, and became the model for much station design elsewhere. Sadly, design standards were allowed to slip on the Underground after World War II, and although there have been a few architectural successes, there has also been some vulgarity in station decor. However, there are now hopeful signs of a return to the pre-war values.

Probably the most famous metro logo of all is that of the London Underground – seen here on one of Charles Holden's Piccadilly Line stations, Bounds Green.
Capital Transport

29

The three photographs on these pages give a few examples of the grandeur of some of the stations on the Moscow system. Shown opposite are ornate details over the entrance to Byelorusskaya station and the 'Moderne' style concourse of Mayakovskaya, opened in 1938. On this page is a view of the concourse between platforms at Komsomolskaya, dating from 1952 but its fancy plasterwork making it look much older. *Country Life*

Especially renowned for their costly and elaborate ornamentation and design are the earlier stations of the Moscow Metro, with their long colonnades, statues, massive chandeliers and walls covered with rare materials from all over European Russia and Siberia. These stations are not to everyone's taste; many find them rather 'over the top' and oppressive, and even the Soviet leader Krushchev (himself personally involved in the building of the Moscow Metro) was critical, in his memoirs, of the design of Red Gates (now Lermontov) station, saying that "the interior has a dirty red colour which can best be described as the colour of raw meat". Others have commented that less money should have been spent on ornament and more on direction signs. Later stations on the Moscow Metro, and indeed on other Russian metros, are markedly less ornate and have aged better.

Showing how most of the Paris Metro stations originally looked, apart from the modern lighting, St Fargeau is one of many stations retaining the white tiling and white-on-blue name signs.
Brian Hardy

Some other stations have been given individual décor as part of modernisation. This is Assemblée Nationale on Line 12.
Brian Hardy

Paris Metro stations are often of simple internal design, with tracks and side platforms all under a wide shallow single-arch roof. Of special interest are the 'Art Nouveau' entrances and canopies which grace many of the early stations in central Paris, and were all designed by a single inspired architect, Hector Guimard. After World War II, the Paris system was badly run down, but a massive modernisation process resulted in many fine new and renovated stations.

There are some metros, including a number in North America, which have taken a strictly utilitarian attitude to station design and left the platforms and structures rather bleak and unadorned. There are others such as the Stockholm system which have given artists and designers a free hand to decorate the platform walls with modernistic paintings and features, sometimes giving rather bizarre effects. The best solution appears to lie between these two extremes, with architecture which is functional without being gaunt, and decor which is bright without being garish.

Top Unusual decoration of rock ceiling at T-centralen station, Stockholm. *Storstockholms Lokaltrafik*

Left and below Also on the Stockholm system, a distinctive view through a series of benchlike granite structures on the platform of Skarpnack metro station and ceramic wall designs showing people's 'ideals, daily life, leisure and work' at Akalla metro station. *Storstockholms Lokaltrafik*

Overleaf – Hankar station on the Brussels metro. *Verbruggen MIVB*

Left – Recent extensions to the Berlin U-Bahn include some very attractive platform decoration; this example is at Lindauer Allee on line U8. *Capital Transport*

Below Official graffiti at Hostafrancs on the Barcelona system. *Capital Transport*

Statuary on the otherwise cold and clinical Königsplatz station in Munich. *SWM*

Statues of the citizenry at Stuyvenbergh station, Brussels metro. *Capital Transport*

A third variation on the theme, this time on the Lisbon system. The station is Campo Pequeno. *Capital Transport*

Enamelled patterns inspired by the coat of arms of the first Earl of Euston. An attractive London station decoration slightly marred by the positioning of the cable run. *Capital Transport*

Ancient and modern on the Tyne & Wear metro. Tynemouth station, a former BR station absorbed into the metro, and Jesmond on the specially built underground section.
North East Studios/ Capital Transport

Interchange between bus and London Underground at Hammersmith. *Capital Transport*

Most suburban metro stations need additional surface accommodation in the form of suitably-sited highway bays for feeder bus services, together with forecourts for cars to set down and pick up the so-called 'kiss-and-ride' passengers and, most importantly, car parks – sometimes on a massive scale – for the many 'park-and-ride' commuters. Waiting rooms are also desirable at exposed open-air stations, especially where there may be longer intervals between trains at certain times of the day.

The track layouts at stations present interesting variations. Most intermediate stations have no more than the two through tracks, but occasionally – as mentioned earlier – there is a crossover for emergency reversing of the service at one end of the station. Simple stations may have an island platform between the tracks, minimising escalator requirements and platform staffing, or separate platforms on each side of the line. At stations where there is regular intermediate reversing of the service, either outside the peak traffic hours or throughout the day, additional tracks are installed, usually between the main running lines, so that a train entering service from the reversing siding does not have to cross a running track.

On some systems, at critical stations where the great volume of the boarding and alighting passengers may hold up trains beyond the normal station stop time (or 'dwell time') and could thus delay the whole service, regulating stations have been installed despite the additional cost involved. Such stations have additional platform faces and tracks which make it possible for a train to overstay its stop time while the succeeding train has already started unloading and loading passengers at an adjoining platform. At some stations, for example Rogier station on Line 2 in Brussels, 'dwell' times are reduced by having platforms on both sides of the train, allowing simultaneous exit from one side and entry from the other.

Platform edge screens and doors are a feature of some newly built metros, making the platforms safer, quieter and better suited to air conditioning where fitted. The examples shown here are in Singapore and the design for London Underground's Jubilee Line extension.
Ian Arthurton/Westinghouse

At terminal stations there may be two, three or four platform tracks, according to the frequency of the service to be reversed there, and the approach tracks include combinations of scissors crossovers, single crossovers and other connections, designed to give the most effective use of the terminal layout. There are often stabling sidings beyond a terminal station, but it is rarely that such sidings are used for regular service reversing. Allowing for train 'layovers' and the time taken for train staff to change ends, it may be reckoned that about 8 trains per hour may be reversed on a single reversing track, about 16 per hour on two tracks and 30–40 per hour on three tracks. However in some cases, as at Elephant & Castle station on London's Bakerloo Line, a full trunk service of well over 30 trains per hour has in the past been regularly reversed on only two tracks by using the process of 'stepping back' the train crews, as explained in Chapter 7.

A few metro systems, notably the Paris Metro and some older North American rapid transit networks such as those of Boston and Philadelphia, have used terminal stations with single-track loops to reverse the services. This seemingly effective layout has, in practice, a number of drawbacks. Despite its severe curvature, the loop has to be quite long and occupies a wide area; there is no opportunity to schedule a rest break for train staff; a train failure on the loop can cause severe dislocation; and there may be coupling problems if all rolling stock units on a line are not facing the same way. In Liverpool, the single-track line of over 3km (2 miles) built beneath the city centre in the 1970s as a terminal loop for the Mersey Railway has three intermediate stations on it which are used largely by commuters from across the River Mersey, rather than unidirectionally by local passengers within the city. A similar position arose with the opening of the London Underground single-track loop extension from the Central Station at Heathrow Airport to the new Terminal 4 in 1986. The London system also boasts a unique loop at a non-terminal station – Kennington – over which part of the Northern Line service is reversed.

So far, we have looked at the functional design and structure of metro stations. Their equipment and finishings – signs, communications, ticket machines, lighting, decor and so on – are considered in the next chapter.

Mention has already been made in the previous chapter of the difficulty of finding suitably located sites of the right size and shape on which to establish the depots required for stabling, inspecting and maintaining the rolling stock. The layout of tracks within the depot should be so designed that trains may enter or leave service to or from the main line before or after the peak traffic periods without conflicting with the movements of rolling stock within the depot itself for servicing and repair. Points, switches and local signals within the depot should be simple and centrally controlled. To avoid derailments, track curves should be as easy as the site will permit, and the layout should be carefully designed so that a single derailment will not block all rail access to the depot or egress from it. For this reason it is especially desirable that the depot shall be double-ended, i.e. with a 'fan' of tracks at each end linking the stabling and maintenance sidings to the running tracks. Single-ended depots are often in trouble. One feature of a modern metro depot is the automatic washing machine, through which trains are usually passed to be washed as they come out of service from the main line; the washing machine track should be paralleled by a by-pass track.

With very few exceptions, rolling stock depots are sited on the surface, and they need protection against local weather conditions. In a cold climate, all the points and switches need to be equipped with electric or gas heaters, and in countries where there are heavy snowfalls, as much as possible of the rolling stock should be stabled in car sheds. Correspondingly, in a particularly hot climate, cars should if possible be stabled in structures with roofs to provide shade, but with open sides. The entire area of the depot needs to be well drained, with adequate pumping and sumps, particularly if – as is often the case – the depot adjoins a tunnel portal.

In addition to the stabling tracks, each depot requires an inspection shed and a maintenance and repair shop, equipped with lifting facilities and with inspection pits below the tracks. With the simplification of metro rolling stock over recent decades, both in mechanical and in electrical terms, the need for great central workshops to carry out complete car overhauls at regular intervals has largely disappeared, and most of such work as remains can be carried out at the rolling stock depots. Also, it may be found convenient to include the depots for track, power supply and signalling maintenance work within the limits of the rolling stock depot site.

For a small metro system – for example, one consisting of two short intersecting lines – it may be considered that only one depot needs to be equipped with a full range of engineering facilities for car maintenance and repair. In that case, it will be necessary to link the two lines by a short connecting track or tracks, so that all trains can reach the main depot as and when necessary; but the lines should run as separate entities in normal passenger operation, and the temptation to run regular passenger trains from one line to the other over the transfer track(s) should be strongly resisted. This arrangement of depot facilities also implies that the line with the fully-equipped depot on it must be built first, even though it may not be the priority line from the passenger's or operator's standpoint.

Left – A Berlin U-Bahn depot waits to start the day's work. A modern large-profile car is seen in the foreground. *BVG*

Below – Rubber tyred trains at La Rose depot, Marseille. *RTM*

British built cars in Hong Kong. *MTRC*

Chapter 5
Equipment and Rolling Stock

The main item of fixed equipment of a metro is the track, and on most of the world's metro systems this consists of conventional steel rails on sleepers and ballast, with the world 'standard' track gauge of 1.435m (4ft 8½in). However, several metros have other gauges, usually reflecting the gauges of the national railway networks in the countries concerned. Thus all the Russian metros are built to the general Russian track gauge of 1.524m (5ft), the Brazilian metros use their national railway gauge of 1.6m (5ft 3in), several of the Tokyo metro lines use the Japanese narrow gauge of 1.067m (3ft 6in), and so on. But there are also a few cases where the metro track gauge differs from the general railway gauge in the same country – examples being the standard-gauge Madrid metro in broad-gauge Spain, the broad-gauge San Francisco transit system in standard-gauge America, and the narrow-gauge Glasgow Underground in standard-gauge Britain.

The rails may be flat-bottomed or bull-headed, and their weight ranges between 36kg/m (73 lbs per yard) and 70 kg/m (over 140 lbs per yard); on most metros, the figure is around 50 kg/m (100 lbs per yard). The rails are often continuously welded into considerable lengths, except on older systems which require joints for signal sections. In tunnel sections, where the temperature range is generally limited, there is little or no problem of heat expansion in the rails. Different forms of rail fastening are used, and in tunnel sections (and sometimes elsewhere) the track may be supported on a concrete slab rather than on timber or concrete sleepers and stone ballast.

The great majority of the world's metro systems feed current to the trains through conductor rails forming part of the track structure. Usually there is only a single conductor rail in each track; this is known as the third-rail system, and the heavy conductor rail usually supplies direct current to the pick-up 'shoes' of the train at a voltage in the 600–825 range. The current rail is normally (but not invariably) placed on the side of the track – usually the outer side, or the side away from the platforms at stations – and is carried on insulators at suitable intervals. The current naturally forms a serious hazard for maintenance staff working on the track (although on many systems, maintenance is carried out at night, after current has been switched off); also, ice can form on the surface of the current rail in the winter in cold countries. Accordingly, on a number of metros with the third-rail system, the shoes on the cars are spring-loaded and pick up the current from the underside of the current rail; this means that the top of that rail can be boarded over or fitted with a moulded insulated plastic cover (as, for example, in Oslo, London Docklands and Helsinki). On one or two networks – notably the London Underground, with its narrow tube tunnels and proximity of the track to the cast-iron tunnel linings – a fourth-rail system is used to reduce earth leakage, with one outside positive rail and one central negative rail, both with top contact. On the half dozen or so metros which employ the Paris type of rubber-tyred trains, the track layout is complicated. The load-carrying pneumatic tyres run on two concrete beams, between which are two normal standard-gauge railway rails. If the pneumatic tyres should deflate, flanged metal wheels mounted alongside them will make contact with the rails and take up the weight of the car. The flanged wheels are also used to guide the car through junctions. To guide the vehicles through curves on plain track, however, there are vertical guide beams on either side of the track, against which horizontal rubber-tyred guide wheels on the car bogies rotate. These vertical guide beams incorporate the current rails, from which there is a side pick-up. There are thus six linear elements in the track, compared with only three in the normal steel-on-steel metro track.

Monorail track, on the other hand, is relatively simple; the monorail's disadvantages are rather in its total height and the cumbersomeness of its car bogies and switching arrangements.

The Kawasaki rubber-tyred system used in the Japanese city of Sapporo may be regarded as a simplified version of the Paris system, since it uses only one vertical guide beam, centrally placed; but this arrangement, too, has drawbacks.

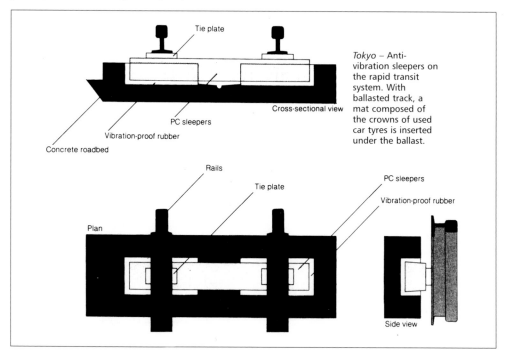

Tie plate

Cross-sectional view

PC sleepers

Vibration-proof rubber

Concrete roadbed

Tokyo – Anti-vibration sleepers on the rapid transit system. With ballasted track, a mat composed of the crowns of used car tyres is inserted under the ballast.

Rails

Tie plate

PC sleepers

Vibration-proof rubber

Plan

Side view

Although most metros use current rails at track level to feed the trains, there are a number of important metro systems which employ overhead catenary wires; these include parts of the Barcelona, Buenos Aires, Milan, Tokyo and Osaka networks, and the whole of the Madrid, Rome, Hong Kong and Seoul networks. These can safely use current at higher voltages (mostly 1,500 volts dc), so reducing the number of substations required. In some instances, where tunnel headroom is limited, a rigid overhead wire or rail replaces the usual catenary, but this can be hard on the collection gear on the cars.

Power for metro systems is normally taken in the first place from the national or local electricity supply, and transformed down at metro substations to the required voltage for the trains. The biggest exception to this practice is the London Underground, which generates most of its electricity requirements at its two generating stations at Lots Road (Chelsea) and Greenwich. The reason is that London Transport has been anxious to ensure that it could get all the trains out of its narrow deep-level tube lines in an emergency in which the general electricity supply had failed. However, with the strengthening of Britain's national electricity system, the abandonment of the London Underground's own power stations is now in sight. The New York City Transit Authority, too, originally owned three power stations, but these were eventually sold to the general power undertaking, which now supplies the New York Subway system.

Overhead current collection on the Tyne & Wear system in Newcastle-upon-Tyne. The front two cars carry a trial livery applied in 1995. *Tyne and Wear PTE*

Metro car, Helsinki, showing underside-contact current rail collection, with protective cover over head of current rail. *Veijo Vänskä*

The power distribution system of any metro must be carefully sectionalised so that in an emergency, current can be cut off from the immediate area of an incident, leaving the rest of the network able to function; this sectionalisation should be linked with the location of interchange stations, emergency crossovers, and so on. There must also be good protection against damage from current leakage. The control of metro power supplies is normally carried out from a central panel, which often forms part of the operational control centre for the whole metro network.

After the track and power supply system, the rolling stock constitutes the third basic element of metro equipment. The design of the rolling stock is critical to the efficient operation of any rapid transit system which may be called on to handle millions of passengers every day. The cars must be rugged if they are to survive thirty years or more of rough daily handling, and their design should take account of the latest tried technology, as well as the experience – good and bad – of other metro operators throughout the world. The cars must be designed with adequate passenger capacity, with a sufficient amount of door space to permit the speedy and simultaneous boarding and alighting of passengers, and with equipment to give rapid acceleration and braking without sacrificing the safety and comfort of passengers.

Shanghai is a recent addition to the list of world cities with metros. German-built trains equipped for 1500v overhead current collection are seen in their depot. *SMC*

Interior of British built metro car for Hong Kong. Limited seating, all longitudinal, means greater crush load capacity in the peak hours. *Ian Arthurton*

As may be imagined, there is a very wide selection of metro rolling stock around the world, ranging from the tiny cars on Berlin's 'small profile' lines, which are only 12.5m long and 2.3m wide, to the massive Hong Kong or San Francisco cars, which are nearly 23m long and well over 3m wide, i.e. about three times the size in terms of floor area. The size of the average metro car lies about half way between these extremes.

There is some variation, too, in the minimum floor area considered to be needed for each seated or standing passenger in the car. The area allotted per seated passenger varies from 0.27 to 0.53 sq metres, while the minimum area per standing passenger is usually taken as about 0.25 sq metres. The London Underground is more generous by allowing 0.3 sq metres per standing passenger, but some systems such as the Moscow Metro reduce the figure to less than 0.2 sq metres under so-called 'crush load' conditions.

The layout of the passenger area of the cars is dictated by a number of factors, including the maximum expected load per car, the average duration of passenger journey, the number and positioning of the car doors, the need for a continuous centre gangway, and even – in a few cases – the need for wheel arches which rise above floor level. For the type of metro system which deals predominantly with a heavy load of short-distance in-town journeys, with an average journey time of under ten minutes, a small number of seats in relation to the total capacity is tolerable. For systems which include a considerable element of suburban operation and have a longer average passenger journey time, a higher ratio of seats to total capacity is required. So, for example, on the Lisbon and Rio de Janeiro metros, on both of which the average passenger journey takes little more than 7 minutes, seats represent only 18 and 19 per cent respectively of the total capacity.

Transverse seating is generally preferred by passengers but at the cost of a reduced standing capacity. All-transverse seating is seen in a Munich metro car. *Ian Arthurton*

By comparison, on the London Underground, which includes several long suburban lines and has an average passenger journey time of over 14 minutes, the seating constitutes as much as 34 per cent of the total capacity; indeed, on one line which operates through central London and then runs out 40km (25 miles) to the north-western suburbs, seating represents no less than 56 per cent of the total passenger capacity of the cars. Usually, where a low ratio of seats is adequate, the seating is longitudinal along the sides of the cars, broken only by the door openings. Where a higher ratio of seating is necessary, some or all of it is transverse.

The usual provision of door openings amounts to two double-leaf doors on each side of a short metro car (as in Berlin or Chicago) or a 'light rapid transit' type of car (e.g. in Vancouver); three or four double-leaf doors on each side of a typical middle-range metro car (as in London, Paris, Tokyo and many other cities); and even five double-leaf doors per side on some 'jumbo' cars such as those in Hong Kong. There are, however, variations to these standards. Some stock, such as the present London District Line cars, have wide single leaf doors. Again in London, the small diameter of the deep-level 'tube' lines means that the wheel arches of the cars rise above the car floor, placing constraints on door openings (as well as inhibiting the seat layout). Metro car doors are of different types; most slide back into recesses, but others are of the jack-knife and 'plug' types. On some systems, particularly those in cold climates with open sections of line, doors remain closed at stations unless individually opened by passengers, using press-buttons on or alongside the doors. Also, in some cars, the windscreens in the vestibules are set back from the door openings; this enables passengers to lean against the windscreens without obstructing the flow of people on and off the cars at stations.

The number of cars required per train is dictated by the traffic demand, frequency of service, and size of car. On some 'light rapid transit' and relatively lightly loaded metro lines, 2- or 3-car trains may suffice. On most of the world's major metros, however, the number of cars per train – at least in the peak traffic periods – may be anything between four and nine cars, the general preference being for 6- or 8-car formations. Exceptionally, on the New York Subway system, 10-car and 11-car trains can be found. On most metros, trains are composed of two or more standard units of two, three or four cars each, the cars in these units being semi-permanently coupled together. In some cases, the units are articulated, with a single bogie between adjoining cars. On some metro systems, or particular lines within systems, it is the practice to run shorter trains in the off peak hours by uncoupling the units and stabling the surplus ones in the depots until they are needed again to make up longer trains for the peak periods; this saves car-kilometres, but the marginal saving in off-peak current costs and in maintenance may be offset by the costs of the uncoupling and recoupling process itself.

The number of electric motors per unit, and their ratings, vary according to the weight of the vehicles, the severity of the gradients on the system, and the desired rate of acceleration and average speed. A high proportion of motored axles, though costly, may increase the overall commercial speed and reduce the round trip time to the point that the service can be run with fewer trains, so producing a major offsetting capital saving. Some metro rolling stock has all its axles motored; among the rest, a typical unit formation might consist of two fully motored cars with driver's cabs at one end, with an unmotored trailer car between them. The variations are numerous, but it is highly desirable that all the units on a metro system – or at least on each line – shall be identical and interchangeable.

Maximum rates of acceleration on metro trains vary between 0.7m/sec^2 in Seoul to 1.48m/sec^2 in Caracas; they are mostly in the $1.1–1.3\text{m/sec}^2$ range. Braking rates are mostly in the $1.2–1.35\text{m/sec}^2$ range, but in some cases emergency braking rates of over 2m/sec^2 are to be found. Of course, unduly high starting and stopping rates can involve risk (or at least discomfort) to the passenger. Braking systems are of various types, including regenerative, rheostatic, electro-pneumatic, disc and magnetic track brakes, and combinations of them.

Hamburg Hochbahn car built in 1968, seen after renovation in 1995. *HHA*

There have been many technical improvements in the design and equipment of metro rolling stock in recent decades. The introduction of light alloys into the construction of metro cars has greatly reduced their weight and brought important energy savings. Similarly, the size of the traction control equipment on the cars has been drastically reduced by the use of thyristors, and chopper control has paid valuable dividends; a subsequent development, the so-called 'gate turn-off' thyristor, has further simplified chopper control and has had special attractions for metro systems, not only by achieving further energy savings but also by giving more precise control of tractive effort and braking. Again, on recent London Underground stock, a combination of micro-processors with multiplex data transmission has greatly reduced the wiring needed for auxiliary circuits in the trains, while at the same time adding a valuable fault-detecting capability. A further simplification has been achieved by the use of rubber suspension systems, not only between car body and bogie, but also between bogie and axlebox. The rubber suspension reduces maintenance costs by eliminating steel springs and other wearing parts; and it also cuts down the noise level.

Open connections between cars provide greater mobility and feeling of security for passengers.
Capital Transport

Overleaf – Operations control centre of BART, San Francisco. The large illuminated wall diagram shows where each train is from moment to moment. *BART*

Other features of metro rolling stock include ventilators, fans or full air-conditioning (depending on the climate and the amount of tunnel and surface line in the system); car heaters (in cold countries); two-way communication facilities between the driver and the central control office (by radio, carrier wave, tunnel wires, etc.); public address equipment, enabling the driver (and sometimes also the central controller) to make service or emergency announcements to passengers in the train; passenger emergency handles or call facilities; in some cases, signal indicators in the driver's cab, in place of lineside signals; and in other cases, equipment for the semi-automatic or even fully automatic operation of the trains. On some modern trains, system maps are supplemented by on-train recorded announcements of location and destination. Also, advertisements can be a useful source of income.

Before leaving the subject of metro rolling stock, mention should be made of the cars operated on the various networks and lines using the Paris 'rubber tyred' system. Just as the track for that system includes more elements than standard 'steel-on-steel' rail track, so the cars also require additional elements. In particular, each bogie includes four rubber-tyred bearing wheels, four horizontally-mounted rubber-tyred guidance wheels, and four steel safety wheels – a total of 12 wheels to perform the same functions as the mere four wheels of a conventional 'steel-on-steel' bogie.

Monorail cars may require a similar proliferation of wheels. Hidden beneath the smooth 'skirt' of the cars of the Haneda monorail in Tokyo are bogies with no fewer than 10 rubber-tyred wheels – four driving wheels plus six guiding wheels. Moreover, in some cases, the monorail's car's driving wheels rise above the general floor level of the vehicle, and where this occurs seating has to be arranged in a back-to-back pattern in the centre of the car, with a consequent loss of passenger capacity.

Having considered the three basic items of equipment needed to get a metro moving – track, power supply and rolling stock – let us now turn our attention to the means by which such movement is directed, i.e. signalling, train control and communications.

The signalling and control system of a metro has two vital functions to perform. The first is to ensure safety of operation; the signalling must be designed to prevent collisions between trains, whether on the same track or on converging tracks at junctions and crossings, and train overruns at terminals or elsewhere. The second function is to keep the traffic moving and enable the best use to be made of the available line capacity.

Typically, urban metro signalling is of the 'automatic block' type, using track circuits and two- or three-aspect colour-light lineside signals (fitted with train stops to bring to a halt any train passing a signal at danger). On the older systems, control of the signals and points at junctions and termini was exercised from local signal cabins, with power operation and interlocking. In the last thirty years, however, there has been a general transformation brought about by technical development, particularly in the field of electronics, and the promoters of the many new metros built in that period have been able to take advantage of this by incorporating the more advanced signalling and train control techniques into their projects from the start. Thus, for example, when the Stockholm 'T-bana' (Underground) was opened in the 1950s, it dispensed with lineside signals (except at junctions) and substituted continuous colour-light signals in the driver's cab. Cab signalling has since been widely adopted on new metros.

On the London Underground, modernisation of the signalling system began with the introduction of 'route control signalling', under which a single manual act in a signal cabin cleared the signals and set the points for a complete route through a junction complex. The next step, in the 1950s, was the introduction of 'programme machines' – electro-mechanical devices which automatically signalled a complete day's train service at a junction or terminal, so doing away

with the need for manned local signal cabins; programme machine signalling, and the computerised signalling that followed it, need no human intervention unless the service is seriously dislocated. On a typical modern system with automatic train control (ATC), all junction and terminal working is done under computer control, and the central control office, which has a diagrammatic picture of the current state of the services throughout the system – in the form of a wall panel or a series of monitor screens – intervenes only in the event of a major incident.

In parallel with the automation of the service control system came developments in the automatic operation of the trains themselves. In the mid-1950s, the Paris Metro began developing the 'wiggly wire' system, consisting of a single continuous wire carrying an alternating current and laid between the running rails of each track in a rectangular zig-zag pattern, together with two induction coils mounted on the train, each over one side of the zig-zag. By continuous frequency comparisons between the induction coils and the irregular sections of the wire, the speed of the train could be regulated. The London Underground started experimenting with automatic train operation (ATO) of a different kind in the late 1960s, and incorporated the new system in the modern Victoria Line, opened in 1968–1971. Under this system, the trains respond to safety codes which are transmitted through the running rails, and to high frequency driving commands which are injected at predetermined intervals on short sections of the track. The trains cannot run unless they are picking up the continuous safety code, and this they cannot do if they are less than a safe distance from the train ahead. The short 'command spots', on the other hand, control the train's acceleration, running speed and braking, so that once the train operator has pressed the dual starting buttons in his cab, the train will accelerate, coast and brake to a stop in the next station without further intervention by the operator. Another form of automatic train operation was devised by the Barcelona Metro in the 1960s, using lights and flanking light-sensitive cells under the cars.

The dividing line between metro and light rail is not always clear cut. The Docklands Light Railway in London is to all intents and purposes a metro, its route being fully segregated throughout. A train is seen at Beckton Park station. Automatic train operation is employed. *Capital Transport*

The ultimate in automatic train operation is the totally unmanned train, and this was first achieved on the rubber-tyred light rapid transit system in Lille (the VAL system) and in Kobe (the Port Island system) in the early 1980s. It has also been achieved on guideway systems such as the quite extensive network within the vast Dallas-Fort Worth Airport (almost a town in its own right) and the unique Morganstown 'Personal Rapid Transit' (PRT) network in West Virginia, USA. Further lines with fully automated operation include the Osaka ICTS line, the Toronto Scarborough line, the Vancouver ALRT line, the various VAL lines in Toulouse, Taipei and elsewhere, and the London Docklands line, though several of these have attendants on the trains for ticket inspection and emergency duties.

There are various ways in which signalling and control systems have been developed to maintain or increase line capacity. One such development is 'speed control signalling', described in chapter 7; this helps to offset the effects of overlong station stops by trains in the peak traffic periods. Another is the concept of the 'moving block' associated with modern automatic train operation, in which the protective block is not fixed but moves with the train, the succeeding train being able to keep up continuously to the safe braking distance behind.

As regards communications, reference has already been made earlier to the need for contact between train drivers and the central control office by two-way radio, carrier wave or tunnel wires; obviously, equipment which allows communication while the train is on the move is preferable to that which depends on stopping the train to enable contact to be made.

Desirably, a metro system should have its own private telephone network linking together every manned establishment in the undertaking. Additionally, all important offices and centres having regular contacts outside the metro itself should be linked to the public telephone network. In the central control office there should also be, if possible, exclusive 'hot lines' to the emergency services, i.e. the fire brigade, ambulance service and police. Other communication facilities in the control office should include closed-circuit television monitor screens, linked to TV cameras in key locations at major stations and other traffic centres around the system. Also, desirably, the control office should have facilities to make broadcast announcements, both general and selective, to the staff and passenger areas of stations and even to passengers in the trains.

This brings us to another element in equipping a metro – the equipment of the stations. Station signs are highly important. The first consideration of the passenger is to identify the station from the street, so it is usual for the metro system's house sign or logo (in many cases a distinctive version of the letter 'M' or 'U') to be prominently displayed over station buildings and entrances, where it can be easily recognised. Within the station, a series of directional signs should be provided along the passenger's route, each one limited to indicating where he has to go next. Taking a multi-line London Underground station as an example, the sequence of signs might read 'Tickets', 'To the Trains', 'Piccadilly Line' and 'Westbound', the last of these signs also listing the stations served by trains from the platform indicated. Signs on the platforms should include station name boards at frequent intervals along the walls, easily visible by seated and standing passengers in the trains. There must also be direction signs indicating the exits from the platform and, in the case of an interchange station, the exits to other lines. Frequently, successive trains from one platform run to different destinations (i.e. the ends of different suburban branches, or intermediate reversing points), and although the trains themselves display their destinations, it is usual in such circumstances to provide illuminated 'Next Train' destination signs over the platforms, easily visible to all waiting passengers. Sometimes these signs, worked from the train description system needed for signalling purposes, are more sophisticated, showing the destinations of the first and second (and sometimes even third) train, together with the waiting time for each. Similar considerations apply where some trains run as 'express' or 'limited stop' services; such services are rarely found on urban metro lines not equipped with extra 'fast' tracks, but where they do operate, the train sequence must be made clear to waiting passengers. The main passenger areas of all stations should be liberally supplied with simple diagrammatic maps of the whole system, to enable passengers to select and check on the best routes to their destinations; sometimes automatic press button route indicators are installed at busy stations for passenger use.

Mention must be made of the widespread use of colour coding and symbols to help metro travellers to identify at a glance the information displayed – one colour for exits, another for interchange facilities, another for emergency alarms, and so on. Some metros also use colour-coding to differentiate between lines at stations, on system maps, and sometimes even on trains (for example in Tokyo and Milan). Internationally accepted symbols may also be used to avoid translating the text of standard signs into different languages.

The fare collection equipment in stations may vary widely according to the fare system used. If there is nothing but a 'flat fare' corresponding to a standard denomination of coin (as was at one time the case on the New York Subway), then passengers have only to insert the coin into a turnstile to gain access to the trains, and there is no need for tokens or tickets, or for ticket-issuing facilities; but as New York found, once the flat fare goes beyond a standard denomination of coin, a token or ticket system has to be adopted. On most metros with zonal or graduated fares, and with special types of multi-ride concessionary tickets for commuters, schoolchildren, the elderly, tourists and others, ticketing facilities have to be provided. Tickets may be issued from a manned booking office and/or banks of passenger-operated ticket machines, equipped with change-giving facilities. At the ticket barrier, the ticket may be checked by an inspector; alternatively, it may be inserted into an automatic barrier gate, which immediately checks from magnetic coding whether the ticket is valid and, if so, lets the passenger through, at the same time presenting him with his ticket back, so that he can use it to get out at his destination station. Gates are of different kinds, including ordinary horizontal turnstiles, tripod or 'milkstool' turnstiles, and four-door and two-door gates (of either the 'normally open' or 'normally closed' type). On some systems, such as the Hamburg Hochbahn, there are no entrance controls, but anyone found by the many travelling ticket inspectors on the trains without a valid ticket pays a severe penalty. The magnetic encoding of tickets, now used extensively, has enabled a wide range of ticketing facilities to be introduced, including all-system or zonal 'passes', multi-ride tickets with 'stored fare' provision (with which the fare for each journey is automatically deducted from their value), and through ticketing between metro systems, main line railways and sometimes also bus systems. Some of these facilities are especially attractive to tourists, who in many cities now form a substantial part of the total metro traffic and travel mainly outside the business peak hours, so contributing to metro revenues at virtually no extra cost to the operator.

Typical metro station entry/exit gates, in this case on the Madrid network. *Ian Arthurton*

One reason for a high degree of automation in the ticketing system is to reduce the number of staff employed at stations, but this can sometimes produce other problems. On the Paris Metro, for example, the number of station staff was so reduced that the crime rate on the system went up alarmingly, and additional metro police had to be brought in to restore and maintain law and order. A similar situation later arose on the London Underground.

Essential to any automated ticketing system is a very high level of reliability in the equipment. Even a one or two per cent failure rate can cause severe trouble when thousands of peak-hour passengers are pouring through the ticket barriers. The management of the London Underground learned the lesson in a rather public way in 1969; there were some red faces when, at the opening of the Victoria Line in that year, Queen Elizabeth could not make her shining new sixpeny coin work the ticket machine.

Mention has already been made of the system-wide communications network required for a metro. In addition, some internal communications are required within each station, including local telephones and a public address system; in some major stations served by several lines, it may also be worthwhile to install a station control room, with monitor screens for the CCTV cameras in the concourses and on the platforms.

There are many other items of ancillary equipment which must or may be provided at stations, including platform seats, vending machines, passenger toilets, public telephones, announcement boards, cleaning equipment, firefighting and first-aid equipment, and collapsible gates at suitable points to secure the stations when no trains are running and to hold back or divert passenger flows as necessary in emergencies. Mention should also be made of the Paris-style platform access gates, designed to close when each train is about to depart and so reduce the risk of accidents from belated attempts to board the cars. These gates are now rare in Paris itself.

Station escalators and lifts have already been discussed in the preceding chapter as integral elements of station design, and so do not need further consideration here as items of station equipment.

While every reasonable effort must be made to make metro travel easy for the passenger, there are some demands which may be difficult if not impossible to meet. For example, more facilities are often urged for the disabled and for people with cycles, wheel-chairs and prams. On a largely deep-level system such as the London Underground, it would take vast expenditures to adapt hundreds of existing stations to meet the demands; so far as the seriously disabled are concerned, it was calculated that it would be cheaper to provide each of them with his or her own car. Also, even if large-scale special facilities were installed, boarding and alighting problems would still cause intolerable delays in the peak hours. Admittedly there may be new lines, or sections of line with surface or shallow stations, where facilities for wheel-chairs or bicycles can reasonably be provided (as in Stockholm and Amsterdam), but it may still be impossible to provide the facilities system-wide or at all times of the day.

The lighting in stations must be of a high standard, and must be carefully designed to give concentrations of light at the critical points (e.g. the ticket machines, ticket barriers, escalators and platforms), while at the same time leaving no dark corners. It is especially important in underground stations that there should be alternative lighting arrangements in the event of a failure of the main supply; these sometimes take the form of a duplicate lighting circuit linked to an independent source of current. Lights must also be installed at regular intervals along the running tunnels, again linked with an alternative source of supply; these tunnel lights are needed not only in emergencies, but also to enable maintenance work to be carried out when the passenger services are not running. There are further lighting problems at rolling stock depots, which are nearly always at ground level; some metros have employed a few pylon-type towers surmounted by clusters of powerful lights, but the modern preference seems to be for a larger number of shorter metal masts around the depot, each topped by a single floodlight which can be winched down the pole for cleaning and maintenance.

Lift for disabled passengers on the Stockholm system.
Ian Arthurton

There now remain two important items of metro plant to be considered, namely drainage equipment and ventilation/air-conditioning equipment. To facilitate drainage, it is necessary that virtually all tunnels should have some gradient, even if it is no more than 0.25 per cent (1 in 400), and that sumps and pumps are installed at the low points in the tunnel. Only at stations should the track be absolutely level, and drainage there is assured by incorporating drainage slopes in the supporting formation. On open sections of line, the water from the track formation normally drains down to a 'cess' on the outside of the tracks, whence it is carried away in pipes to regularly-spaced catchpits, which have to be emptied and cleaned frequently.

Flood prevention is important, particularly in tropical cities where monsoons and cloudbursts may put the streets under feet of water. The sumps and pumps in the tunnels are normally designed to deal only with the ordinary leakage of ground water, so that where there is a threat of flooding, station entrances need to be raised above the level of the surrounding streets, or the whole station must be enclosed in a protective 'bund'. Similar precautions must be taken at tunnel portals and around ventilation openings and shafts. Also, rolling stock depots are often laid out on low ground liable to flooding, and have to be protected by a 'bund'; this was necessary, for example, in building the Northumberland Park depot of the Victoria Line in London – the only part of the line above ground – in the 1960s.

Ventilation and air-conditioning requirements vary greatly according to the form of underground construction and the climatic conditions in the city concerned. On the earliest 'cut-and-cover' underground railways in London (worked at that time by steam locomotives), gaps were left in the tunnel roof wherever possible, but the atmosphere in the stations and tunnels was still smoke-laden and sulphurous. When these lines were electrified, the problem virtually disappeared, and new 'cut-and-cover' lines built in temperate climates now rarely need more in the way of ventilation than an occasional gap in the tunnel roof at points where this does not interfere with the surface infrastructure.

However, if a new line is to be built at deep level, mechanical ventilation will be needed to

Ventilation shafts at an Island line station, Hong Kong. *MTRC*

remove the heat produced by the friction and electrical energy of the trains, as well as the body heat of passengers. In temperate climates, the ventilation shafts and fans are often sited about mid-way between stations, and the fans are normally reversible, acting as pressure fans in the winter and exhaust fans in the summer. In each case, the reverse flow of air takes place through the station entrances and stair, escalator and lift shafts. At some stations, it may be necessary to supplement the inward air flow in summer by fresh air pumped in locally and distributed along the platforms. With these arrangements, it should be possible in a temperate climate to maintain an even temperature of about 21° C (70° F) in the tunnels with three to four changes of air per hour. Where the rolling stock occupies most of the sectional area of the tunnel, as in most single-bore tube tunnels, the trains themselves can cause a considerable 'piston effect' and set up severe draughts in the stations; to deal with this problem, draught relief shafts need to be installed to reduce the air flow through the platform entrances to acceptable speeds.

In tropical climates, even powerful fans may by themselves prove inadequate to cope with the heat build-up in underground stations, so that some form of air-conditioning has to be introduced. In Caracas, for example, every underground station of the metro is equipped with two mechanical cooling and dehumidification units – one at each end of the station – supplying cold air to the public and service areas. The system uses cold water from special refrigeration plants installed at intervals along the lines. In Singapore, it was decided to install platform edge screens fitted with automatic sliding doors to coincide with those of the train; by thus segregating the conditioned air in the stations from the unconditioned air in the running tunnels (which are mechanically ventilated), the platform areas – and indeed the whole station – can be air-conditioned more efficiently. It is interesting to find platform edge screens used in this way to facilitate air-conditioning; elsewhere (e.g. on the fully automatic VAL system in Lille) they have been introduced as a safety measure. Whatever their purpose, such screens demand precision stopping by the trains, so that the train and platform doors coincide exactly.

Despite the problems with equipping air-conditioning in trains that run underground and have frequent opening of doors, in warm climates it is very desirable. The displaced heat can however tend to make other parts of the metro warmer than they otherwise would be. In this Barcelona view the air-conditioning unit can be seen on the roof at the right of the picture. *Capital Transport*

Tunnelling driven in compressed air at Wanchai, Hong Kong. *MTRC*

Chapter 6
Construction

In earlier chapters, we have seen how a metro is planned and designed. The actual process of building the line or lines may be said to begin when the legal powers needed to carry out the project are sought. These powers confer on the metro project management (which may be long-established or freshly set up to build and run a completely new system) the authority to acquire the 'right of way' for the line, if necessary by compulsory purchase; but the management may still have to await executive and financial approval of the project before it can begin to use the powers. Naturally, the political body from which the powers are sought differs from country to country; sometimes it is the national parliament, sometimes the provincial parliament, sometimes a central or regional government legislating by decree or simply using planning procedures. In most cases, people whose property or rights are threatened by the project can lodge formal objections to the grant of the powers, and in any case the powers should provide for reasonable compensation. Often objections can be overcome by direct negotiation between the metro promoters and the objectors.

Taking past British procedure as an example, application for powers was made to Parliament in a so-called 'Private Bill' and considered (together with objections) by a Parliamentary Committee. If granted, the powers covered the acquisition of any properties (or tunnel 'easements' under properties) which might be needed for the project within fixed 'limits of deviation' on either side of the centre line of the works shown in the Parliamentary application. Under recent legislation, this procedure has been simplified and streamlined to reduce delays in the authorisation of major transport and works projects.

When legal powers have been granted, the right of way for the new metro is automatically safeguarded until the actual construction can begin. However, the process of obtaining the powers may be a lengthy one, and the right of way of the proposed line may be threatened by encroachment by new buildings in the meantime. When this happens, money may have to be specially authorised to pay the developers to redesign their projected buildings (or the foundations) to let the metro line through later.

While the legal powers are being sought, the opportunity may be taken to build up the final detailed case for the metro scheme, and to submit it to the central or local government concerned for executive and financial authorisation. The case must cover every facet of the scheme, including the traffic case, the metro concept and design, the proposed services and equipment, the timing and estimated cost of the works, the commercial and socio-economic effects, and a complete financial plan showing the sources of funds and the cash flow position right through from the start of any expenditure and well on into the period of operation.

With the knowledge that the project is to be authorised, a complete works programme must now be prepared. Programming consists of arranging the sequence and timing of all the activities involved in the execution of the project. Its purpose is to ensure that all the work is carried out with the greatest possible efficiency in terms of time and cost. The programme is the instrument for controlling the progress of the project, so that the right steps can be taken when deviations from the programme have to be corrected. The preparation of the works programme involves the analysis of thousands of activities to establish their duration, demands on resources, and relation to each other (i.e. 'network analysis'), so as to co-ordinate them in a time framework, often allowing for several of them to be carried out simultaneously so as to cut down the time needed to complete the project as a whole. The main activities which have to be done in sequence and cannot be carried out simultaneously form the 'critical path' of the programme, and these activities have to be very rigorously analysed to see whether they can be carried out more quickly, so as to shorten the total time taken to complete the project.

The activities covered by the works programme include the final detailed design work; negotiation with other authorities and landowners; acquisition of the right of way; demolition of buildings and diversion of public utilities; preparation of specifications and contracts; the letting of contracts; the civil engineering works; the manufacture, inspection, delivery and installation of equipment; and the final commissioning tests and trial running. As the project progresses, the programme is regularly updated, by computer, to reflect the actual situation and allow any programme adjustment to be made.

Once the metro project has been officially authorised and the funds have been made available, the management can set about using the powers granted to it and acquiring the right of way. This involves much negotiation, and can be the opportunity for linking the construction of the metro with urban renewal and development, including new housing and commercial complexes centred on the metro stations. In the meantime, people displaced from their premises by the metro project must be compensated and found alternative accommodation. At this stage, too, the civil engineering contract documents (detailed working drawings for all the engineering works, bills of quantity, specifications and contract conditions) and the equipment contracts must be finalised. The equipment contracts are based on performance specifications which allow the tenderers to submit prices based on using their own designs and techniques within the constraints of the specification. This form of contract is being extended increasingly to civil engineering work, although there may be some drawbacks.

Now the physical work of demolishing buildings which obstruct the right of way can begin and, with the agreement of the various authorities, a start can be made on the necessary diversion of gas and water mains, sewers and cables. The difficulty of this work could be just as great over 130 years ago as it is today; when the world's first metro was being built in London in the early 1860s, a contemporary writer described the problems in these words: "Railway work in the open has difficulties enough, but the bed of a London thoroughfare has been compared to the human body – full of veins and arteries which it is death to cut. No sooner is the ground opened than these channels of gas and water, of sewers and telegraphs, are seen as close together as the pipes of a church organ. The engineers of the Metropolitan Railway had, to begin with, to remove these old channels to the sides of the roadway, and then to cut their way between, with the delicacy of a surgical operation".

Another difficult problem, especially with cut-and-cover construction under major city streets, is that of diverting road traffic during the works. Diversions are of two kinds – on the surface, using adjacent little-used streets or land, or by means of raised metal decking, prefabricated and easy to erect and dismantle, which can be installed over the construction sites or alongside them. In 1979, when it was building its initial line, the Caracas Metro Company claimed that it was the first time in the construction of a metro that bridges of this kind had been used to divert traffic over areas affected by construction works. This claim cannot, however, be sustained; when the Victoria Line was being built in London in the 1960s, and a big new ticket hall concourse had to be constructed under the very busy Oxford Circus road intersection, a large 'umbrella' of steel panels, complete with road surfacing, was erected over most of the intersection, and carried 44 million road vehicles while the underground construction was in progress beneath it. And there are earlier examples of this technique.

Cut-and-cover construction can also have a blighting effect on shops and businesses in the streets concerned, even though pedestrian access is maintained while the work is going on. It is particularly bad when the works affect the entire length of a major city street for a long period, as in Yonge Street, Toronto, in the 1950s. To overcome this problem, some cut-and-cover metros have been built in short lengths, prefabricated box tunnel sections being built up in the trench before the next section of road is opened up. Another solution, adopted for some sections of the Mexico City Metro, is to build the line along a minor street paralleling the main thoroughfare to be served, but to provide the station entrances in the main street itself.

The preparation of contracts and contract drawings for the works, rolling stock and equipment is a specialised task and is often entrusted to experienced consulting engineers, who may also be engaged to superintend the construction and inspect the equipment. It is usual for tenders to be invited world-wide, and different parts of the project may be carried out by firms from different countries or by international consortia; these then enlist a local contractor who is familiar with conditions in the city and can muster the local labour resources needed. The metro management may also use the consulting engineers to advise them on the award of the contracts. Often the management may opt for a 'turnkey' solution, in which a single engineering group takes on the entire project, sub-contracting parts of it out as necessary. Indeed, some 'design and construct' contracts have even been widened to provide for the contractors, as lessees or agents of the owning authorities, to operate new metro lines for a period of years after their completion.

Following the award of the civil engineering contracts, plant is assembled at the working sites, the initial workforce is recruited and deployed, and construction begins.

There are five main forms of metro construction – surface ('at grade'), open cut, elevated, cut-and-cover and bored tunnel.

The construction of surface lines for urban rapid transit systems is similar to that for conventional railways. First, all obstacles on the route must be removed, down to the subsoil, by means of excavators and graders, taking care that any public utilities are safeguarded. Then the track formation is laid down, followed by the ballast supporting the railway sleepers.

Open cuttings occur where the metro route is at such a level that the space above the right of way cannot be used for other purposes; they also occur where underground lines emerge to continue as surface or elevated lines. The cuttings are excavated normally and, where space permits, the banks are given the natural slope which will ensure their stability; when space is limited, retaining walls are built to support the sides of the cutting.

Where the tracks rise above ground level and room permits, embankments are formed, with bridges where necessary to take the line over highways. In urban areas, however, there is usually little space for embankments, and continuous viaducts are therefore erected; these normally have spans of 20–25 metres (about 65–80ft) between the piers, and are often sited along the median strip of a highway. There must be adequate clearance below the spans for road traffic, and an energy-saving 'hump' profile at stations has the advantage that there is room beneath the platforms to install a ticket hall without reducing the clearance for road vehicles. Passenger access to the ticket hall is provided by a bridge across the road with escalators or staircases up to it on either side.

The columns and piers of the elevated structures are usually supported on pile foundations, and any public utilities affected by them need to be diverted before work begins. The spans are commonly pre-cast and pre-stressed reinforced concrete box beams, one of which is positioned under each track. This arrangement helps where the two tracks separate, for example at stations with island platforms. To avoid disturbing highway traffic, new spans to be installed are usually brought in over the completed section of viaduct and positioned on to the next pair of piers by means of a temporary gantry.

Erection of elevated line for linear-induction transit system in Vancouver. *BC Transit*

Below – Cut-and-cover station reconstruction as part of extension work at Alameda on the Lisbon metro.
Capital Transport

As an elevated structure can be obtrusive in an urban environment, careful architectural treatment and landscaping are essential to make it visually acceptable. Noise screens may also be needed to reduce sound levels.

Several references have been made earlier to cut-and-cover construction, which was widely used for many early metros and is still frequently used today. In the early days, after the surface of the roadway had been opened up, the trench dug, and the sides temporarily shored up, the cutting was lined with brickwork and roofed over by means of transverse brick arches or girders with jack arches, above which the streets were then relaid. Nowadays the work is normally carried out in reinforced concrete. During cut-and-cover construction, various methods of supporting the sides of the trench are used, according to soil and site conditions; they include timbering, steel sheet piling, the use of so-called 'soldier piles', and secant piling (in which concrete piles overlap to form a continuous wall). Struts are needed between the two sides during the work, and ground anchors are sometimes employed. Another method used where appropriate is the 'bentonite wall' (or 'Milan') method, which involves excavating narrow trenches on each site of the route, simultaneously introducing a stabilising slurry (bentonite) into them as support. On completion, the trenches are filled with concrete, displacing the bentonite. Reinforcement of the walls is achieved by lowering a reinforcing cage into the slurry-filled trenches before concreting. The main excavation is carried out between the two concrete walls thus formed, and the roof then erected. A variant of this method – adopted, for example, during work in the Avenida Abraham Lincoln in Caracas – involves positioning roof spans on the completed walls to carry road traffic, and then excavating beneath them.

Sinking of section of immersed metro tunnel, Hong Kong. *MTRC*

There have been a number of unusual adaptations of cut-and-cover construction, one being known as the immersed tube method. Both in Stockholm and in Rotterdam, concrete box tunnels were prefabricated in docks and then floated into position and sunk to provide water crossings for metro lines. But in Rotterdam the technique was carried further; on the line of the metro along the centre of a wide thoroughfare (the Coolsingal), a special canal was excavated and flooded, and the prefabricated tunnel segments were then floated up this canal, sunk into position, connected up and pumped out. Another remarkable feat of underwater metro construction was the laying of the 6km (3.8 mile) transbay tunnel of the Bay Area Rapid Transit system (BART) in San Francisco, completed in 1969; after long soil and seismic studies, the 57 sections of the tunnel were prefabricated and lowered into a trench in the bay floor.

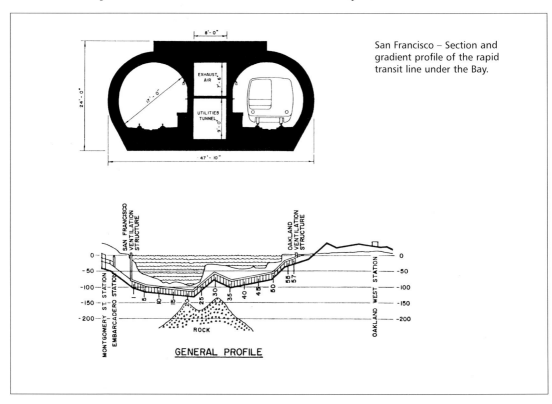

San Francisco – Section and gradient profile of the rapid transit line under the Bay.

Bored tunnels avoid many of the problems of surface and sub-surface disturbance caused by cut-and-cover construction, and do not tie metro routes to road alignments; but they have other problems. In soft ground, it is usual to bore a pair of circular single-track tunnels by means of shields. Starting from the bottom of deep vertical shafts sunk at working sites along the line of route, these shields are erected on the driving alignment and pushed off by rams. Excavation is carried out within the shield, the excavated material being carried by a conveyor belt to light wagons used to remove the spoil. The front of the shield supports the working face while the tunnel lining segments are installed behind it. To drive the shield forward and control the direction, hydraulic jacks are used, which bear on the last installed ring of the tunnel lining. To maintain the correct horizontal and vertical alignment of the shield, its direction is adjusted, using different rams, to correspond to a laser beam which defines the line and gradient profile of the tunnel.

Two improved tunnelling techniques have been developed over the years and widely adopted. In the earlier tube lines, the ring edge of the tunnelling shield cut into the soil, but the actual excavation within the ring was done by gangs of labourers. Nowadays shields with mechanical excavators are used, including so-called 'drum digger shields', having within their outer ring a rotating drum with cutting teeth; the soil is cut by these teeth and guided by scoops and hoppers on to the conveyor belt for removal. The second improvement was in tunnel linings. Originally the lining rings of tube tunnels were made up of cast iron segments bolted together, but in most new construction (except at difficult sites) they now consist of unbolted pre-cast concrete segments; the segments are cast to fit into each other by means of knuckle joints, and when a ring has been placed in position it is expanded outwards against the surrounding soil, so that there are no air pockets around the outside of the tube which need grouting.

Massive Japanese tunnelling shield used in works for the metro in central Lisbon. *ML*

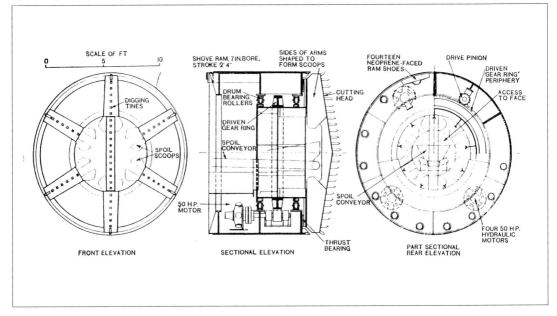

SCALE OF FT
0 5 10

DIGGING TINES

SPOIL SCOOPS

50 H.P. MOTOR

FRONT ELEVATION

SHOVE RAM, 7 IN.BORE, STROKE 2' 4"

SIDES OF ARMS SHAPED TO FORM SCOOPS

DRUM BEARING ROLLERS

DRIVEN GEAR RING

SPOIL CONVEYOR

CUTTING HEAD

SPOIL CONVEYOR

THRUST BEARING

SECTIONAL ELEVATION

FOURTEEN NEOPRENE-FACED RAM SHOES

DRIVE PINION

DRIVEN 'GEAR RING' PERIPHERY

ACCESS TO FACE

FOUR 50 H.P. HYDRAULIC MOTORS

PART SECTIONAL REAR ELEVATION

Diagram of a drum digger shield as used in London for the construction of the Victoria Line.

One of the big problems of boring deep-level metro lines has been that of penetrating loose water-bearing ground. Until fairly recently, most tunnel construction in bad ground has involved working in compressed air, and because of potential health hazards, strict regulations on decompression and medical facilities have applied. Thus when BART undertook construction of its line under Market Street in the 1960s, the whole work had to be carried out in compressed air because of the very high water table in downtown San Francisco, and a special medical centre had to be set up to protect the health of the construction force. Alternatives to compressed air working have been developed, such as chemical treatment of the ground, freezing of the soil by circulating a refrigerant through pipes inserted in it, and lowering of the ground water. These options have to be considered in relation to the state of the subsoil and to their relative cost and effectiveness. In the early 1970s, another method of driving tunnels in water-bearing soil was developed by British engineers, using cutters rotating in a bentonite slurry contained under pressure within a plenum chamber in the face of a Greathead shield; the slurry is circulated, carrying away the spoil from the working face and returning, after cleaning, for re-use. This method, which was successfully tried out in water-bearing Thames ballast, offers the prospect of quicker and cheaper bored tunnels in a wide range of bad ground conditions, and is being increasingly used world-wide.

In tube tunnelling, the platform tunnels at stations are naturally larger than the ordinary running tunnels, and are often built with shields of extra size, and hand-excavated. At junctions, the tunnels take the form of a succession of short lengths of tube progressively increasing in diameter, until the diverging tracks are far enough apart for each to be accommodated in a separate tunnel; this layout is known as a 'step-plate' junction.

When rock is encountered, the tunnels (often horseshoe-section arched tunnels for double track) are excavated by drilling. Where the rock is firm, it may simply be left rough and unlined, or sprayed with a concrete finish. Where the rock is weak, the tunnel is temporarily supported by steel and timber ribs and cladding, and a concrete lining is then built up in situ. A similar system, known as the New Austrian Tunnelling Method, has in recent years also been tried in hard London clay, using mechanical diggers; but a collapse in a tunnel being built for the Heathrow Express line in 1994 led to a hold-up (albeit temporary) in the use of this method at two sites on the London Underground's massive Jubilee Line Extension project. This project is notable for the amount of tunnelling carried out from very large caissons.

A metro junction, Newcastle-upon-Tyne, showing the step-plate tunnel construction providing a staged increase in diameter. *Tyne & Wear PTE*

As the construction of the metro proceeds, the civil engineers give way to the permanent way, electrical, signalling and mechanical engineers, who set about installing their equipment in the completed tunnels and on the completed formations in the open, in a phased sequence laid down by the project programme. Track-laying can be awkward in the confined space of tunnels, especially when the rails have already been welded into lengths of 100 metres or more. One method of handling the problem is to lay the long welded rails along a train of special wagons fitted with bolsters, and hold them laterally between vertical steel pins; in this position they are flexible enough to adapt themselves to the curvature of the tracks over which the train passes en route to the working site. The rails can then be laid rapidly, using a roller device hoisted on a crane jib; the end of a long welded running rail or conductor rail is threaded through the eye of this device, and the crane is then drawn along the length of the rail, the jib being adjusted so that the rail drops on to baseplates, chairs or insulators on the track.

All the equipment supplied has to be inspected before acceptance to ensure that it complies with the specifications. This again is a task often performed by consulting engineers, who may have to make regular visits to the manufacturers to witness tests and check on the quality of their work. Frequently, in the case of rolling stock and other sophisticated equipment, the inspection has to take place in factories in other countries. Naturally, the civil engineering and architectural work must also be inspected and approved before being handed over by the contractors.

With the completion of all the works, the installation of the equipment and the delivery of the rolling stock, a period of trial running (without passengers) can begin. This is essential to ensure compatibility between the different items of equipment, to reveal any problems or deficiencies that may have been overlooked, and to familiarise the operating and maintenance staff with their duties.

In most countries there is, after this, one more step before a new metro line can be opened to the public. Most governments have regulatory agencies which must be satisfied on the standards of construction and safety features of any new railway. Once the appropriate government inspectorate has approved a new metro on these counts, the line can be formally opened and go into business.

With a long line, it may be worthwhile to open it in stages, so that it can begin to earn revenue as soon as possible. Also, if it is expected that the initial metro will in time be expanded into a network covering the city, it is important that there shall be a rolling programme for the construction of the whole system, so as to maintain the impetus and continuity. Successful and economical metro design and construction depend on the build-up of experience and the integration of many disciplines and skills; it is thus most wasteful to stop and start again, and if the time gap is lengthy, the laboriously built-up combination of experience and expertise cannot be quickly or easily reassembled.

In building a completely new metro system, it is usual for a special corporation to be set up to manage the project on behalf of the central or city government promoting it. Alternatively, a consortium may contract to carry out the entire project on a "build-equip-operate" basis. In either case, while the work is going on, the body concerned must also prepare to adapt itself to take over the running of the metro when completed. Among other things, it must appoint the senior operational and maintenance officials at an early stage, so that they can familiarise themselves with the system and its equipment during the construction period, and so be ready to assume control directly the system opens. Often these officials are also sent on attachment to established metro undertakings abroad, to see at first hand the kind of problems that they will have to face when they start running their own lines. Also, junior officials in the various disciplines must be recruited and trained (often, again, by secondment to existing metros) to act in the first place as instructors to the rank-and-file staff, all of whom must be fully competent by the time the metro opens.

In view of the very heavy cost of most metro construction, amounting to several tens of millions of pounds sterling per kilometre of line, there must of course be the closest monitoring and control of expenditure during the construction period. This may be insisted on by the branch of government which authorised the project, since – however large or small the government contribution to subsequent operating costs may be – most (if not all) of the capital cost of a metro is normally met from public funds.

Metro train stabling tracks in rock tunnel, Stockholm. *Ian Arthurton*

Spectacular layout of metro lines at Jurong East station, Singapore. *LTA, Singapore*

Passengers on the Atlanta metro pour off a train for the Georgia Dome. *MARTA*

Chapter 7
Operation

The management organisation needed to run a metro includes a number of administrative departments – secretarial, financial, legal, commercial, and so on – found in any large undertaking and which do not merit special description. The operating and engineering maintenance departments, on the other hand, are highly specialised and are worth a brief study. In the operating department there are several distinct groups of staff; these include the headquarters staff (responsible for timetables, operating regulations, staff duty rosters and staff negotiations), the control staff (responsible for the supervision and operation of the train control and signalling system), the station staff (including supervisors, booking clerks, ticket inspectors, platform staff and station cleaners) and the train staff (train attendants, drivers and guards). The operating department also normally controls any travelling ticket inspectors and sometimes also the metro's own police force. In large metro networks there may be local managers to run individual lines or groups of lines. Responsibility for the rolling stock depots is often divided between the operating and rolling stock departments. Larger metros usually have separate departments for the different engineering functions, but in smaller systems there may be a single technical department covering all the engineering disciplines. Any services that are contracted out are regulated by the appropriate department of the metro authority.

Reference should be made here to the link between the metro operators and the city's bus and tramway operators. Close and continuous liaison is necessary, not only so that the different public transport services shall complement each other, but also so that one form of transport can assist another in emergency. Often the liaison is made easier by the fact that a single undertaking controls all forms of public transport in a city, including all metro and road services.

The basis of metro operation is the timetable, and the compilation of timetables is the art of making the most effective use of available resources. Outside the peak hours, the aim must be to provide services which will be sufficient to attract 'optional' traffic but not so intensive as to make their operation uneconomic; at peak times, it is generally a case of providing as much service as can be devised with the rolling stock and other facilities available.

In designing any regular-interval train service, the number of trains required is arrived at by dividing the headway (train interval) into the sum of the running time for the round trip and the terminal or 'layover' time at each end. The aim must be to keep the number of trains to a minimum. As the peak-hour running time is fixed, the layover time is the only element that can be reduced, and a fractional cut in this time can save the capital and operating costs of a complete train. To achieve this, an arrangement known as 'stepping back' may be adopted, whereby the crew of an arriving train at a terminus, instead of changing ends and taking out the same train, drop back to take out the next arriving train. In the interval between trains, they proceed along the platform to the positions which they will occupy on the next outgoing train, and are thus ready to join it as soon as it arrives. As mentioned in an earlier chapter, this method may have to be used anyway to reverse an intensive service in a terminal station with an island platform and only two tracks. Of course, on a totally automatic system with unmanned trains, such as the VAL lines in France and elsewhere, and the Kobe (New Transit) and Vancouver lines, the layover can be limited to the time taken by the people in the train to alight and the waiting passengers to board.

Apart from the availability and performance characteristics of the rolling stock, the limiting factors in building up the timetable include the track layouts, the minimum train interval permitted by the signalling (usually 1½ or 2 minutes) and staff availability. All these resources are matched as far as possible with the traffic flows on working and non-working days, and at different times of the day. The running time between each pair of stations is fixed, but the station stop time (or 'dwell' time) may vary considerably according to the time of day and location, and this may be taken into account in the timetable.

Hong Kong metro passengers wait in marked queue lines to board the train. *MTRC*

As there is usually a considerable difference in train frequencies between the peak and off peak periods, timetabling the changeover at the start and finish of the peaks can present problems. An abrupt change is not possible, and the timetable must allow for an ordered entry of extra trains into service from the depots in the build-up to the peaks, and a similar return of those trains to depot after the peaks. On lines where train units are coupled together to form longer trains in the peak periods, a similar ordered process of pre-peak coupling and post-peak uncoupling has to be timetabled. The timetable must also allow for all the train crew changeovers required at depot stations and termini.

Reference has already been made in Chapter 3 to the service limitations and problems which may be caused by the interworking of the services of different metro lines over the same pair of tracks, by badly planned branches, and by circular services; these all add seriously to the complications of timetabling.

There are special problems with the correct timing of services which converge or diverge at a flat junction (that is, one without a flyover or flyunder). One example of timetabling techniques is the scheduling of 'parallel working' at such junctions. By this method, a branch train which crosses a trunk line track in one direction is booked over the junction at the same time as the branch train in the other direction. If this working can be adhered to, it is possible to achieve maximum track capacity with the least interruption to the trunk line service by crossing or 'fouling' movements.

One factor affecting the operation of urban rail services is the extent to which 'express' or 'non-stop' running is practicable or desirable. Occasionally, a metro line may have four tracks throughout its trunk section, i.e. two tracks for 'local' (all-stations) trains and two for 'express' (limited-stop) trains. New York has many such lines, with easy cross-platform passenger interchange at the stations served by both types of train. On some sections there is only one track for 'express' services, which run in one direction in the morning traffic peak and in the other in the evening peak, producing a so-called 'tidal' service. On the London Underground, there are a few cases where two different lines run alongside each other for several kilometres, enabling a fast 'non-stop' service to be provided on one and a local stopping service on the other; the line with the non-stopping is always the one going furthest out into the suburbs, so that the longer-distance passengers get the benefit of the quicker service. In any case, when direct cross-platform interchange is provided at each end of the non-stop section, passengers can take easy advantage of the faster running.

Usually, on an ordinary double-track metro line, there is little scope for any non-stop running. With an intensive peak hour service, all trains must as a rule conform to the same all-stations service pattern if valuable track capacity and connections between individual stations are not to be lost.

The scheduling of the first and last trains of the traffic day may require some care, in order to ensure that adequate connections are given with other metro lines and with the early morning and late night services of the main line railways. Sometimes, special staff trains are run before the first passenger train and after the last one, to take early and late turn staff to and from their depots and stations. On most systems, all-night train services cannot be run because maintenance staff must have access to the tracks and tunnels during night hours; but on one or two systems, such as the New York Subway, multiple tracking enables one pair of tracks to carry an all-night service.

The finishing touch to the timetable is the balancing of the rolling stock and ensuring that the correct number of trains of each type are stabled at each depot at night in readiness to form the service the following morning. Where a terminal station is remote from a depot, it may be necessary to stable one or two trains there overnight, ready to start up the early morning service from the end of the line. Exceptionally, on the Paris Metro, trains actually needing maintenance go to depots; other trains are stabled on the line.

In preparing the timetables, a graphic layout of the service is often used, the distances and station locations being shown vertically and the time scale horizontally. The train paths are drawn in, appearing as diagonal lines between stations (the angle varying according to speed) and as short horizontal lines at stations. Nowadays, timetable preparation can be greatly simplified by the use of computers. The working timetables issued to staff responsible for running the service are usually printed in tabular form and contain much extra operational information not shown

Platform scene, Hakaniemi station, Helsinki metro. *Veijo Vänskä*

in the public timetables. Temporary speed restrictions, details of track 'possessions' for engineering works, and other similar variations in normal working arrangements, can be brought to the attention of all the staff concerned by means of special notices.

Closely linked with timetabling is the compilation of the duty schedules for the train crews, the object of which must be to minimise the amount of non-revenue-earning time within the men's duty periods – subject always to the limitations imposed by staff agreements. Time allowances are normally included within the duty periods for booking on and off at depots, walking to and from the trains, examining and preparing the trains for service, meal reliefs, and so on. Overtime and special duties usually entail enhanced payments. Complete duty schedules are prepared for a whole depot or line, showing the rotation of duties between crews, and including provision to cover rest days, holidays and sickness. Train crews themselves usually receive a simple card setting out their own programme throughout from start to finish of their duty, which they can take with them on the train. In addition, on some systems such as the Paris and Brussels metros, digital timers or 'headway clocks' are mounted at platform ends to help drivers to keep to schedule and even out train intervals. Similar headway clocks were at one time used on the London Underground, but they had some demerits and were eventually discarded.

Although the same general factors apply in arranging the duties of other operating staff such as stationmen and service controllers, these duties are less complex because they are not tied to the movement of individual trains. They are nevertheless still limited by the times of starting and ending the service, and by the incidence of the peak traffic periods, when more station staff may have to be concentrated on ticket issue and collection, and on platform attendance. Inevitably, some staff time has to be wasted in the slack hours, but there are alternative duties such as station cleaning which can be carried out in these time margins. On some systems, where station staff have been severely depleted by the automation of ticket issue and control, station cleaning is now contracted out.

It may also be possible, with staff agreement, to schedule a proportion of 'split' duties, in which the period of work is interrupted by a period of rest. Such duties enable a man to cover both traffic peaks in a day, but the total 'spreadover' – the period from the start of the first half of the duty to the end of the second half – may have to be limited.

In the last two decades, economic pressures and automation have led to more and more one-man operation of metro trains. Dispensing with train guards or conductors can not only save money, but also improve the reliability of the service, since the running of a train is then dependent on the availability of only one trainman. The next step is the fully automatic unmanned train, but up to now only a few metros have gone that far. The main problems to be resolved in operating unmanned trains are passenger safety in emergencies (particularly in tube tunnels) and the provision of staff for supervision and assistance.

Station operation is closely related to the incidence of the traffic peaks, when – in addition to the extra staff needed, as already mentioned – extra ticket issuing and control facilities, lifts and escalators may have to be brought into use. At deep-level central area stations which have three escalators in the same or adjoining shafts, two may run up and one down in the morning peak period, with the reverse arrangement in the evening peak, to conform with the main passenger flows:

A vital factor in the economics of urban railway operation is that described as 'line capacity', which is generally taken to mean the maximum frequency of trains which a line can accommodate, although technically the proper definition should be the number of completed train journeys in a given period of time. One problem is that of maintaining peak-hour frequencies despite the increased concentration of the traffic and the resultant tendency towards longer station stops. Reference has been made earlier to the additional platforms installed in heavily used stations on some systems to enable a train to exceed its normal station stop time without holding up the succeeding train. A similar effect can be obtained by the system of 'speed control signalling'; line-side equipment measures the speed of trains approaching a station, and provided that the speed is progressively reduced in accordance with a series of illuminated speed limit signs, a train can be safely kept moving right up to the station, even though the preceding train has exceeded its station stop time. It would of course be better to reduce the length of the station stop rather than attempt to counter its effects, but there are limits in the way of urging quicker movement by passengers. Perhaps the most extreme form of persuasion is that found on some Japanese stations, where squads of men are employed to squeeze passengers forcibly into cars which are already heavily loaded.

Where platforms have been built longer than was necessary for the initial demand, trains can be lengthened later to increase passenger capacity. To lengthen platforms specially throughout a line can, however, be extremely costly, and in any case, the more cars that are added to a train, the less is their individual traffic value; station stop times are still dictated by the most heavily loaded car, usually near the centre of the train.

One factor which materially affects the operating economics of a metro is the extent of the provision made for dealing with failures and delays. Such incidents may be broadly split into two categories. First, there are the relatively minor troubles which cause some blocking-back of trains with the result that the service is, say, five minutes behind schedule at the end of the peak period; an example might be trouble with a set of train doors, in which case the interests of the greatest number of passengers on the line may be best served by detraining the passengers from the defective train and running it empty to depot, rather than by keeping a 'lame duck' in service and so progressively delaying all the trains behind it. The second category of failures comprises those which result in prolonged delays, dislocation of services, the cancellation and emergency reversing of trains, and diversions of traffic; a derailment would be a case in point.

The effect of a delay is, of course, much more serious during the peak hours than at any other time. The repercussions on the close-headway services are more immediate and widespread, while any check in passenger movement at once produces an accumulation of traffic which is afterwards difficult to clear. A major dislocation of service during the peaks can be costly in lost revenue and passenger goodwill, and it is necessary to decide how far emergency facilities (which are expensive to install and maintain) can be justified to minimise the effects of such dislocations.

The actual running of the services, in comparison with the schedules, must be constantly and closely monitored to identify persistent causes of dislocation and delay, so that special efforts can be concentrated on putting them right. It is interesting that in most customer surveys, reliability emerges as the feature of a metro service which is considered of greatest importance by the passenger.

Bi-modal (rail/road) maintenance vehicle on the BART system.
Ian Arthurton

So far we have looked at the operation of the trains. Now let us consider the other major element in running a metro, namely the maintenance of the track, tunnels, structures, rolling stock and equipment. All tracks carrying passenger traffic must be inspected at frequent intervals by permanent way staff, and the necessary day-to-day maintenance is usually carried out by gangs, each normally responsible for a certain length of line. On tunnel sections, all work on the tracks must be performed at night, when the trains are not running and the current can be switched off. Where lines are four-tracked, as in New York, an all-night service can be run on one pair of tracks while the other pair are being maintained. Major track renewals or engineering works may require more time than is available during a single night, and a weekend 'possession' of the track by the engineers may be necessary, with special bus services to bridge the gaps in the metro service while the work is going on. Separate gangs are required for this work, and also for the installation and cleaning of drains, the erection and repair of fences, the renewal of conductor rails, and the loading and unloading of materials from engineering trains.

Various kinds of vehicle may be needed for maintenance of the lines, including flat cars, cars with special supports ('bolsters') for the carriage of rails, hopper wagons, battery-powered locomotives, rail-grinding cars, snow-blowing cars, locomotives equipped to keep current rails clear of ice, rail cranes, ballast tamping machines, inspection trolleys, tunnel cleaning trains (to replace the manual cleaning of dust and grime from tube tunnels), and so on. Much effort may have to go into keeping tracks free of winter ice and snow on metros in cold climates; in addition to the methods already mentioned, passenger trains may be equipped with tanks to dispense de-icing fluid on the current rails, and sections of current rail may be short-circuited during non-traffic hours so as to raise their temperature and thaw the ice on them.

All metro equipment must be inspected and tested at regular intervals, and these intervals may differ considerably between one item of equipment and another, according to their functions and failure records.

In regard to rolling stock, simplification and standardisation over the years have considerably eased the burden of maintenance and overhaul. On major metro systems, the work of the line rolling stock depots was usually confined to stabling the stock, car cleaning, lubrication, inspection, equipment testing and the occasional lifting of a car; major car overhauls were normally carried out at large central workshops. Now, because of the changed nature of modern metro rolling stock, heavy overhauls can be carried out far less often. It is moreover possible to carry out all car overhauls at the line depots, and to transfer equipment renovation and repair to a smaller central workshop, from which complete kits of overhauled and repaired parts can be supplied to the line depots. Of course some extra capacity must be provided to deal with cars or equipment which have failed or been damaged in service; this work points to the need for the standardisation and easy accessibility of parts. On the London Underground, the changes have been quite radical. On some lines, for example, old stock has been modernised and virtually rebuilt as new by outside contractors. On one line, London Underground has 'bought in' a train service; the new trains are owned by the manufacturers, GEC, who are responsible for carrying out maintenance and overhaul work on them.

Chapter 8
The Metros of Europe

The European metro scene is dominated by three of the world's largest systems – those of London, Paris and Moscow, with route lengths of 392 km (244 miles), 201 km (125 miles), and 244 km (152 miles) respectively.

The London Underground consists of two different types of railway. The older lines were built on the cut-and-cover principle, with two tracks sharing a shallow tunnel. The later lines were built by boring separate single-track tube tunnels at deep level through the London clay. Both types of line have the same standard track gauge, but the earlier sub-surface lines have a structure gauge approximating to that of British main-line railways, while that of the tube lines is considerably smaller. There is, however, little difference in the carrying capacity of the two types of line (the variation being in the height rather than the width of the cars), and both types of line come to the surface in the suburbs and continue to their outer termini at ground level or on viaduct.

The cut-and-cover lines were opened between 1863 and 1884, and included a circular line around central London, giving passenger connections between most of London's many main-line railway termini. These lines, which were initially steam-worked, were subsequently extended into the suburbs and all had been electrified by 1906. The first effective bored 'tube' railway was opened in 1890, and by 1907 there were seven such lines criss-crossing the central area; all these lines were operated electrically from the start, and most of them were extended in the years preceding the First World War and in the 1920s and 1930s, when London's suburbs resumed their growth. Some suburbs, such as Morden, Golders Green and Edgware, were virtually created by the Underground.

The original cut-and-cover and tube lines had all been built by private companies, and many of these were amalgamated into larger groups, including particularly the Underground Group. In 1933 a semi-autonomous public enterprise, since known as 'London Transport', was set up to take over and control virtually the whole of the underground railway network and all the bus, tram and trolleybus services in a wide area around London.

A few suburban extensions begun before the Second World War were completed in the late 1940s, but by the 1950s it had become clear that no further extensions to the outer suburbs could be justified in terms of an urban metro type of service. However, increased central area street congestion resulted in the construction of two completely new in-town/inner suburban lines (the Victoria Line and the Jubilee Line) in the 1960s and 1970s. In the Victoria Line, London Transport pioneered the general use of concrete tube tunnel linings and one of the most successful systems of automatic train operation. The Victoria Line also created many new passenger interchanges with existing Underground and British Railways lines, a number of these interchanges being contrived to give easy 'cross-platform' transfer between lines. Now a major extension of the Jubilee Line is in hand, taking the line through two main line termini and the redeveloped Docklands area (see below) to an important interchange point in east London; this is at present the largest engineering project in Europe.

One of the important Underground developments in recent decades was the extension of the Piccadilly Line from one of its western termini to the heart of London's main airport, Heathrow. This extension, 5.6km (3½ miles) long, effectively 'plugged in' the world's busiest international airport to the world's most extensive metro network; it was opened by Queen Elizabeth II in 1977. Later a loop line was added to extend the Underground service to Heathrow's newly-built fourth air terminal. Soon the airport will also be served by a new main line railway, at present under construction.

In 1987, London opened its first 'light rapid transit' line in the former Docklands area of east London, which had become derelict when the port traffic of London moved downstream to the big container port of Tilbury. The Docklands Light Railway was designed to help the redevelopment of the old docks area for housing, commercial, industrial and recreational purposes. This has been so successful that the line has already been extended and upgraded.

Prior to 1970, the London Transport undertaking was answerable to the British government on important policy and financial matters. From 1970 onwards, the undertaking came under the policy control of the Greater London Council, but as a result of growing political interference in the management of the system, the enterprise was taken out of GLC hands in 1984, and reverted to government control. Subsidies received by London Transport have been proportionally much lower than those received by other major city transit systems.

Besides being the world's first metro system, the London Underground is also the most widespread, with five of its eight major lines extending more than 25km (15 miles) out from the city centre. There are fewer passengers than on some other great metro systems, but the average length of journey is generally much greater. Other underground lines in London include the Northern City and 'Thameslink' suburban lines of British Railways and a unique automated tube line operated by Royal Mail for postal traffic.

A large proportion of London Underground's rolling stock has been extensively refurbished during the past decade, the opportunity being taken to combine interior redesign with the installation of improve fire-resistant materials and a new exterior livery using paints which make graffiti removal a fairly simple job. A refurbished 'surface stock' train is seen on the Circle Line at Great Portland Street, while a modernised train of 1972 tube stock is seen on the Bakerloo at Regents Park. *Capital Transport*

A standard three-car train at Cowcaddens on the Glasgow Underground, which reached its centenary in 1996. *Capital Transport*

Other metro systems in Britain include the unusual Glasgow Subway (a narrow-gauge circle line in tube tunnel, converted from cable to electric traction in 1936 and modernised in the 1970s) and the Tyne and Wear Metro (a quite extensive rapid transit system developed in the 1970s, comprising new tunnels under central Newcastle-on-Tyne and pre-existing sections of suburban railway). Not strictly a metro is the Merseyrail system in Liverpool, including the former Mersey Railway under the river to the Wirral Peninsula, together with a one-way loop and underground link line under central Liverpool, built in the 1970s. Mention should also be made of the Liverpool Overhead Railway, a 10.5km (6½ mile) elevated line opened with electric traction in 1893. This became a pioneer of automatic colour-light signalling, and during the Second World War became known as the 'spies' line' because it enabled passengers to see all the wartime shipping movements in Liverpool docks. After the war, traffic declined and the line was eventually closed. There are light rail systems in Manchester and Sheffield, and others are planned in Birmingham, Cardiff, Edinburgh, Leeds, Nottingham and elsewhere.

Gateshead station on the Tyne & Wear metro, with a train in standard livery at the platform. *Capital Transport*

79

The Paris Metro developed somewhat differently from other early metros, largely because of the concentration of population within the old city walls. The lines were built in shallow tunnels and formed a closely-knit in-town network, with stations – many of them interchange stations – at very short intervals. Thus much of the Paris Metro traffic consisted – and still consists – of passengers making very short journeys, who in other great cities would probably use a bus or tram.

The first Paris line (Porte de Vincennes – Porte Maillot) was opened in 1900, and in the following decade several more lines were added, criss-crossing the central area and linking the main-line railway termini. Lines crossing the River Seine did so in shield-driven tunnels or on short viaducts. The track was laid to the standard gauge, but the horse-shoe shaped double tunnels are relatively narrow and this has restricted the width of Paris Metro cars. Curiously, the urban Metro network has right-hand running, whereas the French main-line railways run on the left.

After delays caused by the First World War, development of the Metro network was resumed in the 1920s, but it was not until 1934 that the network was extended beyond the old city boundaries. Two of the underground lines belonged to a separate company (the 'Nord-Sud'), but the main Metro company absorbed them in 1930, and in 1938 also took over operation of the isolated Sceaux line of the French National Railways, which had been built and electrified to main-line standards.

During the German occupation of Paris in the Second World War, the decision was taken to transfer the city's bus services to Metro control; but the full integration of the Paris rapid transit and bus networks did not come until after the war, in 1949, when a single public undertaking, the RATP, took over their combined operation.

There have been several important developments on the Paris Metro in the post-war period, resulting partly from the French government's decision to modernise the system so as to reduce street traffic congestion and provide a showpiece for French technology, and partly from the planning concept of new satellite communities in the outer Paris region. The need for technical modernisation is illustrated by the fact that the last of the pre-First World War Metro cars were not replaced until the early 1980s.

The first major post-war development was the conversion of a number of Metro lines to operation by pneumatic-tyred trains running on wood or concrete beams. Details of the system of operation, and its pros and cons, have been set out in earlier chapters. After prototype testing, pneumatic-tyred operation was introduced on Line 11 in 1956. Some other lines were subsequently converted, but the process was later halted, and it is significant that about two-thirds of the urban Metro network remains conventionally operated, with steel wheels on steel rails. However, the new 'Meteor' line now being built will use the rubber-tyred system.

The second post-war development of note has been the progressive extension of the urban Metro network beyond the old city gates (Portes); the extensions have been short but numerous. At the same time, there has been extensive modernisation of the pre-existing system, especially at stations.

The third major development has been the creation of a new network, the Regional Express System (or 'RER'), to link outer suburbs across the central area by lines of main-line railway type, running in new deep-level tunnels through central Paris and mainly utilising existing surface suburban lines in the outer areas. These lines have longish inter-station distances and fast services, and offer a limited number of good interchanges with the urban Metro system. The individual lines of the RER network are run by the French National Railways (SNCF), by the RATP, or by the two authorities jointly. Some of the RER stations, such as Chatelet-Les Halles and La Defense, involved massive engineering works and are very prestigious.

Yet another area of progress has been that of signalling and train control on the urban Metro. Beginning with experiments with the so-called 'wiggly wire' method in the 1950s, an automatic train operation system has been developed and introduced on most lines, though all trains are manned.

With these improvements, the quality of the Paris Metro system has been greatly enhanced in the last thirty years, while fares have been kept to modest levels. These successes have, however, been achieved only because of heavy capital and revenue support, which has made the Paris system one of the most heavily subsidised in the world.

Paris MF88 stock at Louis Blanc. *Bombardier Eurorail*

The latest stock for the Paris Metro is coded MP89 and is for lines 1 and 11 and the new Meteor line. *GEC Alsthom*

Interior view of an MP73 car, typical of the majority of the trains on the Paris system. *Brian Hardy*

There are four other metro systems in France – in Lyon, Marseille, Lille and Toulouse. The first two of these systems were built in the 1970s and have since been extended. They use the rubber-tyred design developed by the Paris Metro. The Lille and Toulouse (VAL) systems, which have been mentioned in earlier chapters and are rated as light rapid transit lines, also use rubber-tyred cars; but they have two distinctive features. In the first place, the trains are unmanned and the operation is fully automated. Secondly, there are no auxiliary steel wheels and steel track for switching and emergency purposes, as in Paris; instead, the single axles are equipped with steel runners which, at switching points, engage in a central slot formed by two side-by-side rails, in which small switch blades steer the vehicles in the required direction. Also, VAL stations have platform edge screens and doors. Other French cities which operate or are building light rail transit lines include Grenoble, Nantes, Rouen and Strasbourg. There is also a short VAL-type line serving Orly Airport on the outskirts of Paris.

Above – A train on the rack-worked section of Lyon's line C. Other lines on the system use rubber-tyred stock.
GEC Alsthom

Left – Rubber-tyred train in Castellane station, Marseille.
RTM

Top right – Fully automatic trains on the Lille metro.
GEC Alsthom

Right – Another fully automatic metro is the one at Toulouse, opened in 1993.
GEC Alsthom

Turning now to the third of the great European metro systems, the Moscow Metro, we find that it has several unusual features. The best known of these is the sumptuous decor of the older stations, many of which have marble-clad walls, elaborate murals and chandelier lighting; these stations were designed to impress provincial and foreign visitors alike with the achievements of the Soviet state, and were once described by a Londoner as looking like 'the District Line running through a Lyons Corner House'. The second notable feature of the Moscow Metro is that, thanks to the two- and three-shift system on which most Muscovites work, the severe traffic peaks experienced in western cities are largely avoided, and the passenger flows are much more even. The third obvious feature is the very high number of women employed on the Moscow Metro.

It was not until 1935 that the first section of the Moscow Metro, in cut-and cover tunnel, was opened to traffic between Sokolniki and Gorki Park. At the same time, another short sub-surface line was built between Arbatskaya and the Kievskaya main-line station. Excavation for these lines was largely by pick and shovel, the spoil being removed by light railways and wheelbarrows; the work was carried out ruthlessly under the personal direction of Nikita Krushchev, later to become the Soviet leader. By the time of the German invasion of Russia in 1941, a small network of radial lines totalling 26km (16 miles) had been built up. Metro building continued during the Second World War (partly because the tunnels provided air raid shelters) and the first deep-level tube line was opened in 1943. This and later Moscow lines were built at a depth of 30–50 metres (100–160ft), i.e. considerably deeper than a typical London tube line. By 1945, the Moscow Metro had increased its route length to 40km (25 miles), and by 1954, with the completion of a circular line to supplement the previous radial lines, all the main Moscow railway termini were linked by Metro. One casualty of the period was the early Arbat line with its four stations and bridge over the River Moskva; this short section was abandoned in 1953 when a parallel deep level tube line opened between Kievskaya and Kurskaya (another main-line railway terminus).

Since the 1950s, the Moscow Metro has continued to expand steadily, mostly by extensions into the suburbs, and the system now carries more passengers than any other in the world, the traffic amounting to over 3,000 million passenger journeys a year. However, the average journey may be shorter than on certain other major metro systems.

Because the tube tunnels have been driven through fissured limestone with a considerable water content, there have been fears of corrosion of the cast-iron tunnel linings, and use is now made of segmented concrete linings, which are expanded outwards against the surrounding soil profile in much the same way as on London's Victoria Line in the 1960s. The Moscow Metro – and indeed all metro systems in the former Soviet Union – use the broad Russian gauge of 1.524m (5ft) and, to accommodate this while keeping the car wheels completely below floor level, the minimum internal diameter of the tunnels had to be fixed at 5.46m (just under 18ft).

In recent years the Moscow Metro has developed and introduced an automatic system to monitor and improve the condition of the air in its tunnels; the system provides continuous control of the temperature, moisture content and purity of the air underground.

Apart from extensions to their existing Metro system, the Moscow authorities are also considering the possibility of a high-speed 'regional' network, similar in concept to the Paris RER system.

In addition to the Moscow Metro, there are no fewer than twelve other metros in operation in the former Soviet Union – in Ekaterinburg, Nizhni Novgorod, Novosibirsk, Samara, St Petersburg, Baku (Azerbaijan), Erevan (Armenia), Kharkov (Ukraine), Kiev (Ukraine), Minsk (Belarus), Tashkent (Uzbekistan) and Tbilisi (Georgia). All but two of these (Novosibirsk and Tashkent) are in Europe and all of them conform to the technical standards of the Moscow system in respect of track, power supply, rolling stock design and so on. The Erevan and Tashkent Metros have a special feature; the tunnels had to be designed to withstand earthquakes up to force 10 on the Richter scale.

Opposite – Moscow cars dating from 1976, seen outside their depot. Current is collected from the underside of the covered conductor rails seen with a layer of snow.
Moscow Metro

Left – Later Moscow metro stations are plainer than the over-ornate ones for which the system is well known. This is Marksistskaya, opened in 1979 and an important interchange point.
Moscow Metro

The largest Russian metro outside Moscow is that of St Petersburg, which consists of four lines. The first line, connecting several main-line railway termini, was opened in 1955, and to avoid tunnelling through the deep layer of water-saturated sand and silt on which St Petersburg rests, the tunnels were driven at a depth of 60m (200ft) or more through the underlying clay. As in Moscow, the older stations were lavishly decorated, while the later ones are more restrained in design. St Petersburg Metro was the first system to introduce platform edge screens and doors in its stations.

The metro boom is still on in the former Soviet Union; virtually all the existing systems are being progressively expanded, and several new metros are being built or planned.

The Berlin U-Bahn, like the London Underground, has two sizes of line – 'Large profile' and 'Small profile'. It is one of Europe's oldest systems, the first line (across the city from the west to Warschauer Brücke) having been opened in 1902; most of this line was on rather ponderous viaduct, while the underground sections were built by the cut-and-cover method. When German sovereignty was restored after World War II, the Berlin system was cut in two by the political division of the city, with most of the network lying in the western sector and under the control of the BVG (Berlin Transport Board). A comparable organisation, the BVB, controlled public transport in East Berlin. Since the reunification of Germany, the two systems in Berlin have been brought together again under the BVG, and through services restored. In West Berlin, the BVG some years ago put into service on its Line 4 a system of full train automation developed in West Germany under the title of 'Seltrac'; but although the system has proved reliable in operation, the BVG decided to leave a man on each Seltrac train to deal with breakdowns. West Berlin has also operated a short stretch of novel magnetic-levitation line (the 'Magnetbahn'), similar to the Birmingham Airport link in Britain; but the line had to be abandoned when the site it occupied was redeveloped. The Berlin Underground ('U-Bahn') is complemented by an extensive suburban railway ('S-Bahn') network.

Above – A small-profile Berlin U-Bahn train at Görlitzer Bahnhof. *John Humphrey*

Left – The latest U-Bahn stock for the large-profile lines breaks away dramatically from the design of its predecessors. *AEG*

Berlin Zoologischer Garten station, with a train of S-Bahn hand-worked door stock in the platform. This is a major bus and rail interchange in the city centre. *Capital Transport*

The Berlin S-Bahn's latest stock is in course of delivery and should enable the withdrawal of all remaining pre-war trains by the year 2000. *AEG*

The interior of the new Berlin S-Bahn trains is a different world compared with that of the trains being replaced; unusually first and second class accommodation is provided. A first class section is seen in the foreground. *AEG*

The Hamburg metro is known as the 'Hochbahn' because a considerable proportion of the original system was constructed on viaduct; nowadays it also includes many cut-and-cover tunnel sections. The Hochbahn forms part of the 'Hamburger Verkehrsverbund' (HVV), an association of public transport operators in the Hamburg region to which the suburban railway system (the 'S-Bahn'), the bus operators and the ferry operators also belong. Besides co-ordinating their services, the members of the HW have integrated fares, marketing and ticketing arrangements, and pool their revenues. The HW was the model for a number of similar public transport associations in other major conurbations in West Germany.

Other metro systems in Germany include those of Frankfurt (Main), Munich and Nuremberg. In addition, there are a number of German cities with suburban rail ('S-Bahn') systems which run through the central city areas, often in tunnel, but which are not used predominantly for short-distance journeys within the central areas. There are also numerous German cities, including Bochum, Bielefeld, Bonn, Cologne, Duisburg, Düsseldorf, Essen, Hannover, Karlsruhe and Stuttgart, which have light rapid transit or pre-metro lines, often including tunnel sections.

Hamburg: a Hochbahn train at Borgweg station.
HHA

Frankfurt U-Bahn trains at Ginnheim terminus.
John Humphrey

Certainly the most unusual and interesting urban transit system in Germany is the 13.3km ($8^1/_3$ mile) long suspended railway or 'Schwebebahn' in the Ruhr city of Wuppertal (formed by the amalgamation of the towns of Barmen and Elberfeld). Opened as long ago as 1901, the line consists of twin monorail tracks mounted on overhead girders; the cars are suspended from roof-mounted bogies. In places the line is carried above the River Wupper, where, to quote an earlier commentator, 'it provides a striking, though hardly beautiful, addition to the landscape'. Above the river, the line is borne on massive A-shaped supports, but over some streets the supports take the form of an inverted U. Since the Second World War, the line has been modernised and new rolling stock introduced, making possible one-man operation of the trains. The drivers have cab TV monitors to show the situation on station platforms. Further modernisation, including conversion to automatic operation, is planned.

Above – A metro train built by MAN for Munich stands in the Bavarian snows.
Stadtwerke München

Left – The suspended monorail in Wuppertal provides a pleasant ride but the heavy infrastructure dominates large areas of the town.
WSW

Moving to Spain, we find the capital, Madrid, well provided with metro lines. The first section was opened in 1919, and cut-and-cover methods were largely used to build horseshoe-shaped single-track tunnels. One unusual feature was the current collection system adopted; the rolling stock was equipped with current collection arms of the trolleybus type. Although there have been regular extensions of the Madrid Metro over the years, the number of passengers declined seriously for a while, and priority has since been given to new rolling stock rather than continued rapid expansion of the network. Interestingly, the track gauge is almost identical to the standard European gauge, and thus differs from the broad gauge of the Spanish main-line railways.

In Barcelona, the underground lines making up the metro system have different gauges and power supply systems, as a result of their different company origins. The main east-west line (Line 1) has the Spanish main-line gauge of 1.674m (5ft 6ins), with power supplied by a conductor rail at 1,500 volts dc. The four other lines of the city network have the standard track gauge of 1.435m (4ft 8½ins) and third-rail power supply at 1,200 volts d.c., or overhead supply at the same voltage. Lines U6 and U7 (forming part of the regional rail system) have standard-gauge track, with power supplied by catenary at 1,200 volts. Most of the Barcelona network has been built in shallow double-track tunnels, and the system has been expanded regularly over the years; the planned objective is a network of some 120km (75 miles). All of the Barcelona city network (Lines 1–5) and Lines U6 and U7 are underground with the exception of short stretches of Lines 1 and 5 in the west of the city, where depots are situated. Barcelona's novel experiment with a light-actuated automatic train system has been described in an earlier chapter.

Train of the latest Madrid metro stock, shown awaiting commissioning in a maintenance depot. *Ian Arthurton*

The latest stock on the most recently opened line of the Barcelona metro, line L2. This is the present southern terminus at Paral-lel. *Capital Transport*

About 4km (2½ miles) of a metro in Seville had been built when the authorities decided to call a halt to the works and await the results of a comprehensive study covering all forms of transport in the city. The first tunnel section of the Bilbao system has now been opened. In Valencia, a metre-gauge metro-type link was opened in 1988 across the city centre, enabling trains from pre-existing suburban lines to serve the inner city. The only other metro in the Iberian peninsula is that of Lisbon, which was mostly built by the cut-and-cover method and conforms to general metro standards. It was opened in 1959 and has been expanded progressively ever since. A second Portuguese metro is planned in Oporto.

Stations on the new metro in Bilbao have been designed by Sir Norman Foster & Partners. This is Abando. *CTB*

A three-car train on the Valencia metro, a short metre-gauge city centre connection to suburban railway lines. *GEC Alsthom*

Below – Picoas station on the Lisbon metro, with third-rail current collection. *Metropolitano de Lisboa*

The Low Countries display a range of urban rail transit systems, from underground tramways to full metro systems. The Belgian cities – Brussels, Antwerp and Charleroi – have opted to develop their metro systems in two stages. In the first (so-called 'pre-metro') stage, tunnels or elevated lines of full metro dimensions are built in the central area, and tramway lines are diverted through them; in the second stage, the trams are replaced by full-scale metro trains. Of the three cities, only Brussels has so far reached the second stage, and then only on part of the network. In Holland, the two largest cities – Rotterdam and Amsterdam – opted for full metro systems from the start, despite the problems involved in tunnelling under major waterway systems; the unique method adopted to build the Coolsingal section of the Rotterdam Metro has already been described in Chapter 6. Both cities' metros have complementary light rail ('Sneltram') lines and Amsterdam is developing a light ring line. Utrecht also boasts a light rail network.

Brussels has a mixture of metro and 'pre-metro' tram services in the centre. This metro train is on a former tram service.
Capital Transport

Heysel station at the end of one of the Brussels metro lines with the famous Atomium in the background.
Capital Transport

Above – A Rotterdam metro train at Spijkenisse Centrum station. *RET*

Right – A train on a Rotterdam 'Sneltram' line, which mixes reserved and roadside track. *RET*

A German-built train leaves one of Amsterdam's somewhat austere metro stations. *John Laker*

Italy also has several metro systems. That of Rome, the capital, had a curious origin; the first line was built to serve a World Fair which was due to be held in 1942 but never took place. Construction stopped during World War II but was resumed after the war, and the line was opened in 1955 despite the fact that its original purpose had disappeared. A second line was built in the 1970s, but its construction was delayed to avoid damage to historic buildings and archaeological remains. The system is now being further expanded.

The Milan Metro, the first section of which was opened in 1964, is notable for the novel method of cut-and-cover tunnelling employed in its construction, involving the use of bentonite slurry in building the tunnel walls; the process has been explained in Chapter 6. Also, a special resilient form of track support was devised to reduce vibration on the section of line adjoining Milan's historic cathedral. A cross-city railway tunnel is now being built to link existing suburban lines.

Naples has a small metro, opened in 1992, which is to be extended. The city already had a section of underground railway known as the 'Metropolitano', but this is not strictly an urban metro. Genoa also has a light transit line, and other Italian cities operating or planning light metro lines include Bologna, Florence and Turin.

Italian-built stock on the metro in Naples. *Ansaldo*

A driving car for Rome's line B at the carbuilder's factory. *Breda*

Interior of Rome metro car. *Breda*

One of the major metro systems in Europe is the Stockholm 'T-bana', all of which has been developed since the Second World War. The T-bana is notable among metros for having pioneered such things as cab signalling, integrated metro/new town planning, 'double-deck' cross-platform interchange, and novel methods of tunnelling in extremely difficult soil conditions. Rock tunnels were built where possible, but much of the rock was found to be faulty, and at one station (Gamla) where there is regular shifting of the ground, the booking hall was provided with expansion joints allowing movements of up to 250mm (10 ins) and was sealed in a copper and plastic 'sandwich' to keep out ground water. At other sites with water problems, construction involved chemically freezing the soil and working in compressed air.

Another interesting Scandinavian metro is that of Oslo, where the trunk section of a group of suburban lines on the east side of the city was carried below the city's central axis to make contact with an existing network serving the western suburbs. The final link involved a short underground extension of the western network to Sentrum, where easy passenger interchange was established with the loop terminal layout of the eastern lines. Through services between the east and west lines are now being developed. A particular feature of the Oslo metro lines is that the bottom-contact current rail has its top and side covered in a moulded fireproof polyester and glass-fibre sheath.

In another northern city, Helsinki, similar metro construction problems to those of Stockholm were encountered; underground stations were blasted out of rock, and artificial freezing of the soil was necessary where the line had to be built through a moraine-filled cleft below ground water level. In Copenhagen work has started on a 22km 'mini' metro.

Above – Stockholm trains in old and new liveries pass between Gamla Stan and Slussen in September 1994. *Brian Patton*

Left – Oslo Underground pantograph-equipped car at Majorstuen in July 1991. *Brian Patton*

In Central Europe, metros are to be found in Vienna, Prague and Budapest. Since 1898, Vienna has had an urban railway system of the light rapid transit type, known as the 'Stadtbahn'; this is partly in tunnel. After the Second World War, it was decided to put some in-town sections of the extensive tramway system into tunnel. Finally, in 1969, work began on the nucleus of a full-scale metro system (the 'U-bahn'), and several lines of that system are now in operation. To co-ordinate all the varied public transport facilities in the Vienna area, a new association, the 'VOR', came into being in 1984.

Prague has had a metro since 1974, and the three-line network is still being developed. In building cut-and-cover sections, the 'Milan' method of wall construction was used. For tube sections, Soviet-built tunnelling shields were employed, and the concrete tunnel linings were of Soviet pattern. The Prague Metro is now one of the busiest in Europe.

The Budapest Metro has had a long and chequered history. The first line (which was also the earliest metro on the European mainland) was opened in 1896 under the resounding title of the 'Franz Josef Electric Underground Railway'. Because the tunnel was extremely shallow, the rolling stock had an oddly squat appearance. In 1950, a start was made on a modern metro line, designed to have lavishly-decorated stations on the Moscow model, but three years later the work was stopped, and the resources diverted to housing and industrial development. When work resumed in 1963, much more utilitarian and economical standards of station design were adopted. The line was finally opened in 1972, and further sections have since been added. Until the 1980s only Soviet-built rolling stock was used, but more powerful Hungarian-built cars with chopper control and regenerative braking were ordered in 1984.

As in Prague and Budapest, there was considerable Soviet involvement in the Warsaw Metro, the first line of which opened to full public service in 1995; among other things, the Soviet Union made a gift of 90 Russian-built metro car to the project. The Bucharest Metro (opened in 1979) and the Sofia Metro (under construction intermittently since the 1980s) also show some Russian influence.

Another urban passenger railway in Europe deserving mention is the Athens-Piraeus line, which was the first railway in Greece and was electrified in 1904. Built to link the Greek capital with its port of Piraeus, the line was extended in the 1950s from its in-town terminal to Kiphissia in the north-east. The central section is in tunnel. The line has undergone modernisation, and two further metro lines are being built.

Finally, mention must be made of the light metro which has been running in Istanbul since 1989. A new 'heavy' metro has been under construction there since 1993. Metro development in Asiatic Turkey is referred to in Chapter 11.

Vienna U-Bahn train climbing ramp from Ober St Veit on line 4 towards Hütteldorf. *Alan Blake*

A Soviet-built train on the Prague metro. *Orbis*

Another train of Soviet construction seen on the Budapest system. *BKV*

Below – Siemens-AEG train with locally built stainless steel bodies on the Athens-Piraeus metro line. *ISAP*

A New York City Transit train built in the early 1990s. *GEC Alsthom*

Chapter 9
The Metros of North America

Although metros originated in Britain with the opening of the London Metropolitan Railway in 1863, America was not far behind.

New York's first metro – an elevated railway – was in operation along 9th Avenue by 1870; for two years, this line was operated by cables, but steam locomotives were then introduced, and further lines were subsequently built in Manhattan and north into the Bronx. All these lines were consolidated in 1879 to form the Manhattan Railway Company. The elevated lines built in the growing boroughs of Brooklyn and Queens were steam-operated from the start, and almost all of them came together under the control of a different company, known as the Brooklyn Rapid Transit or 'BRT'.

By 1901, all the elevated operations in New York City were under the control of the two concerns – the Manhattan Railway in Manhattan and the BRT in Brooklyn. The Manhattan Railway alone owned a total of nearly 132km (82 miles) of elevated structure. Although the elevated lines carried many passengers, their heavy metal structures dominated the street environment and obstructed downtown road traffic. The trains ran at second-floor height, and there was much noise, dirt and grime.

The cross-Hudson lines (PATH) are operated independently of the NYCTA network. *John Laker*

So it was decided to take further urban railways underground, using cut-and-cover methods (often in rock) to build tunnels for the new electrically-operated 'subway' lines. Work on the first subway began in 1900, and in 1904 the line was opened from Brooklyn Bridge via City Hall and Broadway to 145th Street; later it was extended into the Bronx and under the East River to Brooklyn. The subway was built by the City, but was operated by the Interborough Rapid Transit Company (IRT), which was formed in 1902 for the purpose. Because the new subway operation covered the territory of the Manhattan Railway, the IRT took a lease of all Manhattan Railway property and the 'Elevated' in Manhattan was integrated with the subway.

Between 1913 and 1920, a further group of subway lines was built by the City under the so-called 'Dual Contracts' – one between the City and the IRT, and the other with the BRT (which eventually became in 1923 the Brooklyn-Manhattan Transit, or BMT). Until the completion of the subways under these contracts, the BRT had only a toe-hold in Manhattan by running across Brooklyn Bridge with one leg of its 55km (34 miles) of elevated route.

As the subway system expanded, the earlier downtown elevated system declined; most of the remaining elevated lines lay outside the central area. All the steam-worked elevated lines had been electrified between 1900 and 1904.

The year 1932 saw the opening of a third group of rapid transit lines built by the City. Neither the IRT nor the BMT would bid for the operation of this new subway system unless agreement could be reached to abandon the 5 cent fare. So the City decided to run the subway itself and coined the name Independent (IND) for the operation.

In 1940, the City of New York bought out all the interests of the private IRT and BMT undertakings, and the whole network was then operated by one concern – the Board of Transportation – with three divisions (the IND, IRT and BMT). The acquisition of the BMT included practically all the bus and streetcar operations in Brooklyn, and a proportion of those in Queens. In Manhattan, however, the IRT did not control the bus and streetcar operations, which were dominated by the Fifth Avenue Coach Company and the Third Avenue Railways. These did not come under municipal control until the New York City Transit Authority (NYCTA) was formed in 1953 as successor to the Board of Transportation. It is this authority which still operates New York's subway and bus systems today. Since 1968, however, the NYCTA has come under the jurisdiction of the Metropolitan Transportation Authority set up by the State of New York, which also has other transport enterprises such as the Staten Island Rapid Transit system and the Long Island Railroad under its control.

In parallel with the development of the subway and elevated railway system extending northwards and eastwards from Manhattan, a group of tube railways was built westwards from Manhattan under the Hudson River to link the City of New York with the State of New Jersey. The first of these tube lines, which were owned and operated by the Hudson and Manhattan Railroad, was opened between the 19th Street/Sixth Avenue terminus (New York) and Hoboken (New Jersey) in 1908, and the Manhattan end was extended to 33rd Street by 1910. A second pair of tunnels was opened in 1909 to link Manhattan with Jersey City, and the service was extended over Pennsylvania Railroad lines to Newark two years later. A north-south tunnel on the New Jersey side, linking Hoboken and Jersey City, was opened in 1909. After long financial struggles, the Hudson and Manhattan Railroad eventually went bankrupt, but in 1962 the States of New York and New Jersey stepped in and set up a new body, the Port Authority Trans-Hudson Corporation (PATH) to take over the Hudson tube lines. Thanks to investment in new track, trains, signalling and power supply, PATH achieved a transformation in this system, which now provides an attractive modern service.

There have been important post-war developments in New York's main subway system (the NYCTA system) as well, including the construction of a new East River tunnel and a connecting tunnel under Central Park, the building of the 22km (14 mile) Second Avenue subway and the 5km (3 mile) East 63rd Street line, and an extension of the Jamaica line in Queens. Sadly, however, the NYCTA subway system was generally inadequately maintained in the post-war years and by the late 1970s was in a run-down condition, with unreliable services and outmoded practices and equipment. In 1981, following the New York State Legislature's declaration of a 'transportation emergency', massive funds were voted for the modernisation and rehabilitation of the New York subways. The programme covered all types of infrastructure and equipment; in particular much new rolling stock was bought from Canadian, French and Japanese manufacturers, and existing cars were given heavy overhauls.

There are two features of the New York Subway system which are not general in other rapid transit systems around the world. One is the multiple-tracking of trunk sections of line, allowing two tracks to be used for 'local' (all-stations) trains and another one or two tracks for 'express' (limited-stop) trains; where there is only one track for express services, these use it in different directions in the morning and evening traffic peaks. The second feature is that many lines (not just the 'tidal flow' express tracks) have bi-directional signalling. Both the multiple-tracking and the two-way signalling have helped to mitigate the effects of serious breakdowns on the system.

Another feature of the New York Subway is the fare collection system. With a flat fare, it was originally possible for passengers to use a single coin to work the turnstiles giving access to the platforms. With the post-war inflation, however, the flat fare had to be raised above a single denomination of coin, so that a token system had to be introduced. Now a fully automated fare collection system is being installed.

In terms of route length, the New York Subway and the London Underground are much the same in size, but the New York network has more track length and carries the larger number of passengers. However, the average journey length is markedly higher on the London Underground, and London buses carry many more people than their New York counterparts.

One last post-war phenomenon of the New York Subway was the wholesale coverage of the system – stations and trains (inside and out) – with graffiti, many of them elaborate and bizarre. The NYCTA was eventually able to keep this down; PATH had already largely succeeded in keeping graffiti off the Hudson tube lines.

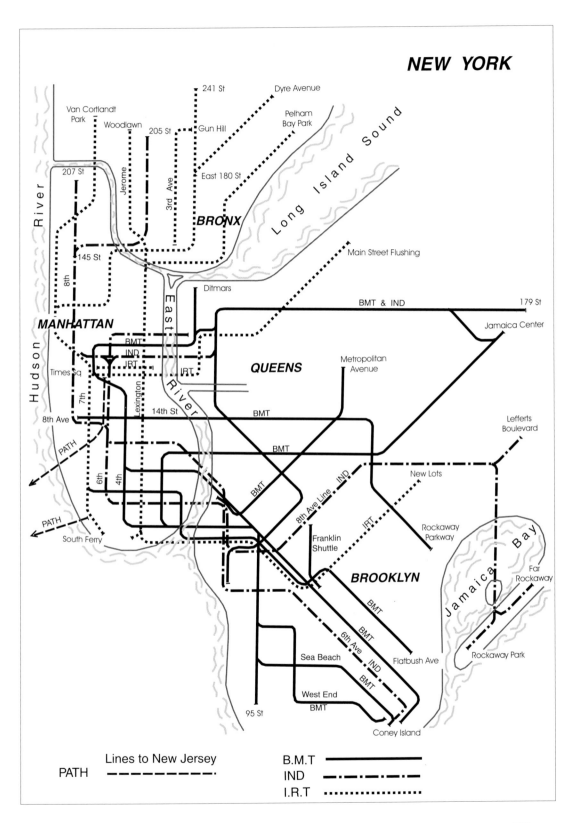

NEW YORK

241 St
Dyre Avenue
Van Cortlandt Park
Woodlawn
Pelham Bay Park
205 St
Gun Hill
Jerome
3rd Ave
East 180 St
207 St
BRONX
Long Island Sound
145 St
8th
Main Street Flushing
Ditmars
East River
MANHATTAN
BMT & IND
179 St
Jamaica Center
BMT
IND
IRT
IRT
QUEENS
Metropolitan Avenue
Times Sq
7th
Lexington
14th St
BMT
8th Ave
Lefferts Boulevard
PATH
6th
4th
BMT
New Lots
8th Ave Line IND
IRT
PATH
BMT
Franklin Shuttle
Rockaway Parkway
South Ferry
Jamaica Bay
BROOKLYN
Far Rockaway
BMT
BMT
6th Ave IND
Sea Beach
Flatbush Ave
BMT
Rockaway Park
West End
95 St
BMT
Coney Island
Hudson River

	Lines to New Jersey		B.M.T	————
PATH	– – – – –		IND	–·–·–·–
			I.R.T	··········

After the New York system, the next American metro in order of importance is probably that of Chicago. Up to 1943, Chicago had a network of elevated railways – including the famous 'Loop' around the downtown area, on which trains ran 'on sight' (without signals) – as well as a unique underground freight railway, but no underground passenger lines. In 1943, the first passenger 'subway', the State Street Line, was opened, and this was followed in 1951 by a second subway, the Congress Line. The unusual continuous downtown platforms on these two lines have been described in an earlier chapter. Later extensions of the Chicago rapid transit network have used the median strip of major highways, one such line built in this way being the extension to Chicago's O'Hare Airport, one of the world's busiest airports.

San Francisco's extensive post-war rapid transit system (BART) opened in stages in the 1970s and included many novel features. To test these new concepts of track, rolling stock and signalling design, a special 7km (4½ mile) test line had been built at Diablo in the 1960s. One result of the studies was the adoption of the broad gauge of 1.676m (5ft 6ins) for the system; another was the use of aircraft construction techniques in the building of the cars. The automatic train control and fare control systems, too, were sophisticated and previously untried in service. When passenger operation began, serious design faults became evident, and there were long delays before these could be corrected and trains could be allowed to operate through the long tube tunnel section under the Bay; BART's experience was a warning against 'going it alone' in metro design. The San Francisco system is more of a regional rapid transit network than a conventional urban metro, as the average distance between stations is no less than 3.4km (2¼ miles), and the trains operate at a commercial speed of 80km/hour (50 miles per hour). A series of three substantial fare increases commenced in 1995 to help finance a ten-year programme to renew the system and its rolling stock and open major new extensions. BART train services to the airport, some way from the system at present, are among the plans. In addition to BART, San Francisco also operates an extensive light rail network ('Muni').

Chicago rolling stock of 1991 at Madison/Wabash in October 1996. Note the close proximity of the next station. *Brian Patton*

The Bay Area Rapid Transit system, San Francisco, is a wide-gauge metro providing spacious train interiors. Sliding doors provide passenger connections between the cars. A 1970s built train is seen in December 1995. *Capital Transport*

Two long-established American metros are those of Philadelphia and Boston. The earliest line in Philadelphia was opened in 1908, with the unique track gauge of 1.581m (5ft 2¼ins) and with a reversing loop at its western end involving severe curvature and heavy gradients. The line was partly in tunnel, but was later extended on viaduct to the north-eastern side of the city. Subsequent lines, mainly in tunnel, were built to the standard gauge, making impossible the working of trains to and from the original line.

Boston was the first city in North America with an underground railway; its earliest metro line, opened in 1901, ran in tunnel under the city centre, although the outer sections were on viaduct. Two later lines were also built with their central sections in tunnel. In addition there is a light rail network.

Philadelphia: a platform attendant on the Broad Street subway line at Fern Rock station. *SEPTA*

A train on the Boston Red Line at Ashmont in July 1994.
Brian Patton

The most important remaining metro in the USA is that of the federal capital, Washington DC. Planned as an eventual 166km (104 mile) system, the Washington Metro has been opened section by section since 1976; nearly 90 per cent is now complete, but there have been problems with Government funding. Also, while the system looks modern and impressive, there have been a number of design problems which have reduced the reliability of the services. These include difficulties with the earlier batches of cars (which were built on the same principle as those of San Francisco), with the 'stored fare' ticket system, with the concealed lighting in stations, and with some of the tunnel linings, which had serious water leaks. The actual construction work also caused problems; for example, certain long stretches of cut-and-cover work badly disrupted traffic on major streets for years on end. Like San Francisco, Washington tended to go 'too far too fast' in some elements of its metro design; this was in stark contrast to the outlook of the New York Subway authorities at the time.

Other American cities with full-scale metro systems are Atlanta, Baltimore, Cleveland and Miami. The Cleveland system had the distinction of being the first in the United States to provide a direct metro link between a city and its airport.

Archives – Navy Memorial station in Washington with a train leaving. Concealed lighting on the platform softens the effect of the structural lining. *WMATA*

Atlanta metro – train on the airport line.
GEC Alsthom

New terminal platforms at Johns Hopkins Hospital station on the Baltimore metro. *MMTA*

A train on the conventional Miami metro, which is complemented by a downtown 'people-mover' line. *MDT*

In Los Angeles, the wheel has turned full circle. In its early days, the sprawling city was criss-crossed by a network of street railway lines known as the Pacific Electric system, but with the advent of the freeways and the predominance of the automobile, those lines were considered obsolete and were abandoned. Now the worsening road traffic situation has led to the construction of new metro and light rail systems for Los Angeles, the first lines of which are already in operation, with extensions under way. The Blue Line and Green Line are light rail; the Red Line is a heavy rail tube line.

Apart from full-scale metros, there are more than twenty networks of the 'light rapid transit' (or upgraded streetcar) type in existence, under construction or planned in the USA. These range from small VAL-type or ALRT 'people-mover' systems in downtown Detroit, Jacksonville and Miami to the unique Morganstown Personal Rapid Transit system in West Virginia, a short monorail in Seattle, and a regional network in Dallas.

Montreal – interior of a metro car. The dot matrix indicator on the right displays the day, date and time in French and English. *STCUM*

Canada's two largest cities, Toronto and Montreal, have developed metros since the Second World War, both of which have distinctive features. The Toronto system – the first line of which, the Yonge Street line, was opened in 1954 – has the rare track gauge of 1.495m (4ft 10⅞ ins), i.e. slightly over the world standard gauge. The cut-and-cover construction of this line showed how much disruption may be caused by opening up a main street from end to end, rather than in stages; there were heavy demands for compensation from the shops and other businesses along Yonge Street. The second line, the Bloor-Danforth, crossed the first line at right angles, but was linked to it by a loop connection running under University Avenue. The link was designed to permit through services between the two lines, but train working complications led to the segregation of services on the two lines and reliance on passenger interchange between them. Later extensions of the Toronto metro were planned jointly with the development of new suburban centres, the new stations forming an integral part of the developments.

In the French tradition, Montreal opted for a rubber-tyred metro on the Paris model. This has been generally successful, although there were a few early troubles which might be attributed, at least in part, to the rubber-tyred system. In the decades following its opening in 1966, the Montreal Metro was progressively extended, but in 1985 it was suggested that any new lines should be built with conventional steel-on-steel, partly to enhance the export potential of the Bombardier company in Quebec.

Surface and subsurface scenes on the Toronto metro, both with a distinctly North American look. *John Laker, Ian Arthurton*

The most interesting metro development in Canada in recent years has been the installation of the new 'intermediate capacity' or ALRT (Advanced Light Rapid Transit) system, first in a metro feeder line in Scarborough (Toronto) and then in a complete 29km (18 mile) metro for Vancouver. The ALRT concept was developed by the Urban Transportation Development Corporation (a Canadian company founded and originally owned by the Ontario government), and includes innovations such as steerable bogies to reduce track and wheel wear, moving-block automatic train control to minimise the headway between trains, and linear induction motors to simplify propulsion and braking, and make them independent of the adhesion between wheel and rail. The designers claim that ALRT represents the best value for money in many situations where metros with intermediate capacities (8,000–25,000 passengers per hour per direction) are required. One city outside Canada to adopt the ALRT concept was Detroit, where a short elevated circular line of this design is in operation in the central area.

There are two other transit systems of the light-rail type in Canada, in the Albertan cities of Edmonton and Calgary. The Calgary authorities reported in 1983 that 40 per cent of the transit users were former bus users, while up to 20 per cent had switched from car to rapid transit; another 30 per cent or so were completely new riders.

North Westminster station on the Vancouver ALRT line. *Westbury Marketing*

Below – Winter conditions on the high-technology linear-induction Scarborough line in Toronto. *UTDC*

The most heavily used metro in North America is that of Mexico City, which is closely modelled on the Paris Metro; all its lines have pneumatic-tyred rolling stock of the French type, and the limited dimensions of the cars (due to the low axle-loads of the rubber wheels) result in crush loading conditions for passengers for much of the day. The first section of line was opened in 1969, and within ten years the network had grown to over 50km (32 miles) and was carrying some 900 million passengers annually. By the late 1980s, the system had grown threefold and the annual passenger count to some 1,400 million, producing overloading of up to 47 per cent, with 250 passengers travelling in a car designed for 170 people. Despite financial stringency in recent years, the Mexico City Metro continues to expand in an endeavour to meet the ever-increasing demand.

Two other Mexican cities – Guadalajara and Monterrey – have introduced light rail systems. Guadalajara at first built some sections of tunnel through the city centre in the 1970s; these were provisionally used by trolleybuses until light rapid transit trains were introduced in 1989. The Monterrey lines form an elevated and segregated system, opened in 1991.

Narrow rubber-tyred stock on the Mexico City metro. *STC Metro, GEC Alsthom*

Chapter 10

The Metros of South America

By far the oldest metro system in South America is that of the Argentine capital, Buenos Aires. Because of its mixed origins, the Buenos Aires 'Subterraneo' has considerable technical differences among its five lines. The first line, from Plaza Mayo to Primera Junta, was opened in 1913–1914 and was run by the Anglo-Argentine Tramways Company; it has an overhead wire current supply, at 1,100 volts dc. The second line was opened in 1930 and was operated by the Buenos Aires Central Terminal Railway; it has third-rail current distribution at 550 volts dc. The remaining three lines were opened between 1930 and 1944, and were run by a Spanish company; these have overhead current supply at 1,500 volts dc. The whole system has the world standard gauge of 1.435m (4ft 8½ins), not the broad gauge of most Argentine main-line railways. In 1939, a corporation was set up to co-ordinate public transport in Buenos Aires, and all metro lines in the city were operated from 1963 by a State body known as the 'Subterraneo de Buenos Aires.' There have been a number of short extensions to the system since the 1960s, and a light rapid transit line has been added to the network. In recent years, the system has been restored to the private sector, as part of the Metrovias consortium.

If Argentina was the first South American country to have a metro, it is Brazil which has been the most active in metro development in recent years, with modern rapid transit lines in Sao Paulo, Rio de Janeiro, Belo Horizonte, Recife and Porto Alegre, and a light rail system in the capital, Brasilia.

In Sao Paulo, which has grown rapidly and is now one of the world's largest cities, metro construction began in 1968, and the first line was opened in 1974. Further lines have been built, but expansion of the network has been slowed down by financial stringency. Financial limitations have been so severe that costly air-conditioning was omitted from some new cars, which have pressurised air ventilation instead. The bored tunnel sections of line have a diameter of 5.7m (18ft 8ins) to accommodate the generously-proportioned rolling stock running on the broad-gauge (1.6m or 5ft 3ins) Brazilian track. Computer control of the chopper traction system makes for smooth and efficient train operation. And the windows in the Sao Paulo Metro cars are bullet-proof!

Left – A viaduct section of the North-South metro line in Sao Paulo. *IRJ*

Above – Rio de Janeiro Saens Pena station, with passengers boarding and alighting on opposite sides of the train. *Metro de Rio de Janeiro*

Metro construction in Rio de Janeiro began at much the same time as in Sao Paulo, and the same technical standards were adopted for the first line, which was opened in 1979 and now runs from Saens Pena in the west, via Central, to Botafogo in the south. Plans for Line 2 had to be scaled down because of funding difficulties; at present it runs as a 'pre-metro' line (with third rail current collection) from Estacio (on Line 1) as far as Engenho da Rainha. Plans for expanding the Rio Metro have been frustrated by financial difficulties and by consideration of a cheaper alternative technology – the air-powered 'Aeromovel' system – but extensions of both lines are now in hand.

The other three major Brazilian metros – in Belo Horizonte, Recife and Porto Alegre – have been built to full metro standards and were opened in 1985/86. Moreover, all three include up-graded sections of old railway routes, and use overhead power supply at 3,000 volts dc.

Two-level interchange metro station in Sao Paulo. *Metro de Sao Paulo*

A modern train for Santiago's Paris-style metro. *GEC Alsthom*

The only rubber-tyred metro in South America is that of Santiago, the Chilean capital, which has a two-line system built on the Paris model. The decision to install a metro in Santiago was taken on the grounds that traffic congestion had brought the average speed of road vehicles in the city centre down to only 12km/hour (7½ miles per hour). Most of the Santiago Metro is in vaulted reinforced concrete tunnel.

A further system in operation in South America is that of Caracas, the capital of the oil state of Venezuela. The city lies in a long valley, and before the advent of the metro, private cars were used for no fewer than 45 per cent of journeys to work in the central area; as may be imagined, road traffic congestion was severe, despite the provision of a costly and elaborate urban motorway system. The metro was planned as a three-line network, and priority was given to the 'backbone' line along the valley from Propatria to Palo Verde. In 1983, the first year of its operation, the initial section of this line, as far as Chacaito, carried 55 million passengers. Work has since proceeded on the rest of the system, and the annual ridership now exceeds 300 million. The system is of conventional steel-on-steel type, and almost every method of construction has been used in building it, including the 'bentonite wall' method developed in Milan.

Colombia also has been planning metros in its principal cities of Bogota and Medellin. The latter city was given priority and work began in 1985, following an inquiry which rejected allegations that the US$627 million construction contract had been awarded irregularly to a Spanish-German consortium. The first line was opened in 1995.

Another South American city with a recently completed metro is the Peruvian capital, Lima.

French-built stock on the Caracas metro. *GEC Alsthom*

Left – A train enters a station on the Medellin metro, Colombia. *ETMVA*

115

Tokyo Subway platform scene. *Ian Arthurton*

Chapter 11
The Metros of Asia, Australasia and Africa

The metro scene in Asia is dominated by the Japanese city networks, and notably by that of Tokyo, which serves one of the world's largest urban populations. The Tokyo metro system started with the opening of the Ginza line (now Line 3) in 1927, and expanded as the city grew in the 1930s. The early lines were built by different undertakings, which were amalgamated in 1941 to form the Teito Rapid Transit Authority (TRTA), funded by Tokyo City and Japanese National Railways. After the Second World War, Tokyo resumed its growth, and a measure of its development is provided by the daily average of commuters, which went up from under half a million in 1955 to nearly 2 million in 1980. To help combat the severe road congestion, the metro network has been further expanded, and in 1960 the Tokyo municipal government became directly involved by opening the Asakusa line (Line 1), operated by its own Transportation Bureau (TBTMG). At present, the Teito undertaking has eight lines and the municipal undertaking four lines, the combined route length of the whole network amounting to some 240km (150 miles). Despite daunting costs, further extensive construction is under way or planned, including one small-profile tube.

Partly because of its mixed origins, and partly because of interworking with some Japanese main lines – with their narrow gauge of 1.067m (3ft 6ins) – and with standard gauge private railways, the Tokyo metro network is unique in the variety of its equipment and operating methods. Some lines are narrow gauge, some standard gauge; some are self-contained, others have through services to and from the main-line railway system and private suburban lines; some have overhead power supply, others third-rail; and the signalling systems range from ordinary automatic block type, with three-aspect lineside signals and train stops, to an automatic train control system in which the driver merely monitors the running of his train.

TOKYO SUBWAY NETWORK

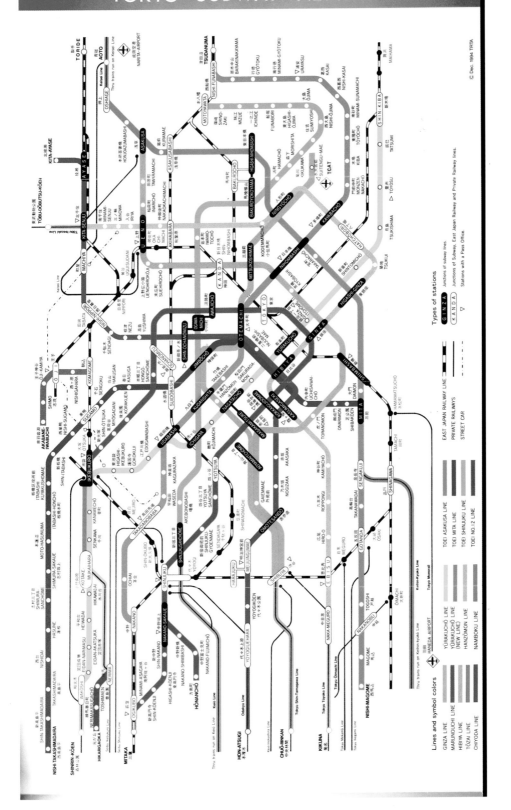

© Dec. 1994 TRTA

Interior of a Tokyo Subway car, with smartly upholstered seats and banner-type advertisements.
Ian Arthurton

The great majority of the Tokyo network is in tunnel, and because of the soft ground over much of the area, virtually all the lines are of the shallow subsurface type. Some severe constructional problems had to be overcome. At Shinjuko, for example, where the station had to be built under a 10-track section of the Japanese Railways without disturbing the main-line services, it was necessary to cast the tunnel walls in trenches, underpin the tracks and erect a roof before actually excavating the metro tunnel itself.

In addition to the metro proper, there is an interesting straddle-type monorail line – mentioned in an earlier chapter – from the edge of Tokyo's city centre at Hamamatsucho to Haneda Airport. For a while after its opening in 1964, this line was something of a white elephant, but with increasing congestion on the parallel motorway, steps to attract commuters and improved interchange arrangements at Hamamatsucho, it now carries a worthwhile traffic. Tokyo also now boasts a fully automated rubber-tyred 'people-mover' line, the Yurikamome line, opened in 1995.

Train depot of the Tokyo monorail line to Haneda Airport, showing the cumbersome switching arrangements.
Tokyo Monorail

Other Japanese cities with metro systems are Chiba (suspended monorail), Fukuoka, Hiroshima (light rail), Kitakyushu (monorail), Kobe, Kyoto, Nagoya, Osaka, Sapporo, Sendai and Yokohama. Several of these provincial city networks have novel features. Kobe, for example, besides having a part-underground and part-elevated line across the city to join its main surface railways, as well as a growing municipal 'subway' system, also has a guideway system serving the Port and Rokko Island areas which was designed for driverless computer-controlled operation. When this new transit system was opened in 1981, however, all the trains carried a driver, mainly to gain passenger confidence; but in August 1982 the drivers were withdrawn and the lines now operate entirely automatically.

The Sapporo system, referred to in earlier chapters, has two distinctive features. Opened in 1971, it was the first rubber-tyred metro to use a central guide-rail instead of side-rails; and as Sapporo has heavy snowfalls (and indeed hosted the Winter Olympic Games of 1972), the elevated sections of line were enclosed in circular aluminium tubes to eliminate the adhesion problems of rubber tyres on snow. Hiroshima also has a light rail system and rubber-tyred guideway line.

Yokohama: scene on the 'New Transit' rubber-tyred system serving the waterfront. *KNT Yokohama*

One of the great metro success stories of Asia is that of Hong Kong, where the British-designed and British-equipped three-line system of over 40km (25 miles) has had an enviable construction record. The first section of the so-called 'Modified Initial System' (MIS) opened one month ahead of schedule in 1979. The full MIS opened seven weeks early in 1980. The Tsuen Wan line opened no less than seven months ahead of time in 1982; and the Island line, running along the north shore of Hong Kong Island itself, opened five weeks early in 1985. The system has a number of special features, including a 1.4km ($^7/_8$ mile) immersed tube tunnel under the harbour, some of the largest metro cars in the world, steel rails fixed in concrete 'slab' track, and an elevated section in Tsuen Wan which was totally enclosed to keep train noise out of the surrounding housing estates. The financial results of the Hong Kong Mass Transit system have been greatly assisted by profits from judicious property development schemes along the lines. The ticketing facilities include a stored-value system which has accounted for about a half of all journeys on the MTR network; the fare for each journey made is automatically deducted at the entry gate and the ticket returned with the residual value marked on it. This facility was extended to the Kowloon-Canton Railway, Hong Kong's original railway, which has been modernised and electrified in parallel with the metro development. Now Hong Kong's public transport is going over to the latest contactless 'Smartcard' fare collection system. A further metro line is being built under Hong Kong harbour, together with a rail link to the new Chek Lap Kok airport on Lantau Island, and an extensive light rail system has been created in Tuen Mun new town.

British-built train on the successful Hong Kong metro system. *GEC Alsthom*

THE HONG KONG METRO

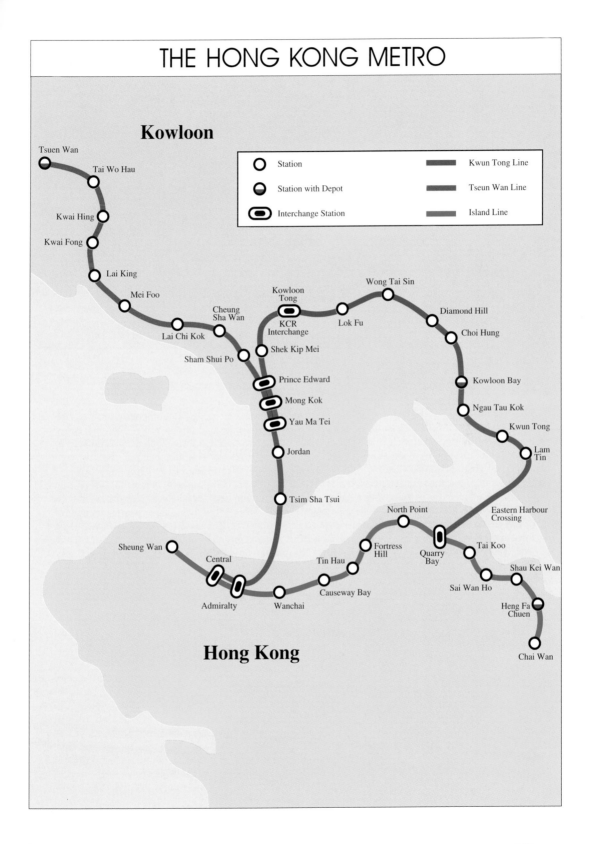

Kowloon

	Station		Kwun Tong Line
	Station with Depot		Tseun Wan Line
	Interchange Station		Island Line

Tsuen Wan
Tai Wo Hau
Kwai Hing
Kwai Fong
Lai King
Mei Foo
Cheung Sha Wan
Lai Chi Kok
Sham Shui Po
Shek Kip Mei
Kowloon Tong
KCR Interchange
Lok Fu
Wong Tai Sin
Diamond Hill
Choi Hung
Prince Edward
Mong Kok
Yau Ma Tei
Jordan
Tsim Sha Tsui
Kowloon Bay
Ngau Tau Kok
Kwun Tong
Lam Tin
Eastern Harbour Crossing
North Point
Fortress Hill
Tin Hau
Quarry Bay
Tai Koo
Sai Wan Ho
Shau Kei Wan
Sheung Wan
Central
Admiralty
Wanchai
Causeway Bay
Heng Fa Chuen
Chai Wan

Hong Kong

High-capacity train on the Seoul Metro. *GEC Alsthom*

Another Far Eastern city which, like Hong Kong, has expanded phenomenally in the post-war years is the South Korean capital of Seoul, which is now one of the world's largest cities. Seoul's first metro line, with through running with the national railway system, was opened in 1974. The subsequent lines (including a circular line) are self contained metro lines of conventional type. Korea has had to rely on foreign suppliers for much of the equipment – power supply and signalling equipment from the USA, rolling stock equipment, track materials and workshop plant from Britain, and a Japanese input into the cars themselves (which have nevertheless been built in Korea). There has been similar foreign involvement in the development of the metro in Pusan, the important port facing across the Korea Strait towards Japan. Both Seoul and Pusan metros continue to expand. New metros are also under construction in Inchon and Taegu. Communist North Korea also boasts a conventional metro in its capital city, Pyongyang.

Despite the size of its principal cities, China has been comparatively slow in the development of metros, partly – one may imagine – because of the high numbers of bicyclists on its city streets. However, congestion eventually became a serious problem, and the capital, Beijing (Peking), opened its first metro – a 24km (15 mile) cut-and-cover underground line running straight from east to west – in 1969. By the 1980s, the line was carrying a quarter of a million passengers a day and saving commuters between the city centre and the western industrial area an hour a day in comparison with bus travel.

While this first Beijing line was relatively unsophisticated in its operation, the second line – a 16km (10 mile) loop in the form of an inverted U, linking two stations on Line 1 – has computer-directed automatic traffic control and train operation systems, which are understood to have had technical troubles since the line was opened in 1984. In recent years, British and French advice has been sought on the updating and improvement of the network. Stations on Beijing's second line are more decorative than those on the original line. For instance, the station under Yonghe Lamasery is fitted with classical Chinese chandeliers of the kind used in the ancient lamasery itself. Also, noise-absorbing materials have been used in station ceilings and walls on the second line. Work has been going on to expand the Beijing Metro, and at least two further lines are planned.

Chinese-built train on the second (loop) line of the metro system in Beijing. *MTRC*

Another metro in operation in China is in the port city of Tianjin. This short line was opened in the 1980s, work on it having been maintained despite the effects of the massive earthquake which destroyed the adjacent city of Tangshan in 1976.

Shanghai, China's largest city, has plans for a 176km (110 mile) system, the first short line of which was opened for trial running in 1993 and to full public service in 1995. Further sections should be opened later in the 1990s, but the progress of the whole metro depends on funding, which is limited. There are plans for a two-line metro system in Guangzhou (Canton), and one line is being built. No fewer than eight other Chinese cities are now building, or planning to build, rail-based public transport networks; they include Harbin and Chengdu.

In India, plans were drawn up for metro systems in all the four main cities – Calcutta, Bombay, Delhi and Madras – but only in Calcutta has there been substantial progress, and even there work has been greatly delayed by soil and flooding problems. In the 1960s, British and American consultants recommended an elevated system for Calcutta, to avoid problems associated with the waterlogged soil, the great heat and humidity, and the monsoon floods. However, acting on subsequent Russian advice, the Indian authorities decided to build the first 16km (10 mile) line, from Dum Dum to Tollyganj, mainly in cut-and-cover tunnel, with one short section in bored tube. Instead of buying 12,000 tons of sheet piling from the USSR as originally intended, the Indian engineers decided to use the diaphragm wall method wherever possible, but endless problems with water seepage and fall-ins delayed the work. The last straw came in the summer of 1984, when there were heavy floods in the city. Shopkeepers on the route of the metro had the bright idea of reducing the flooding in their premises by breaking down the brick protection walls around openings in the roof of the metro tunnels. As a result water cascaded into the tunnels, submerging trains and station equipment and causing major damage. After repairing the damage, the Indian authorities called in experts from overseas to advise on how to expedite the work, and by the end of 1984 a partial service was running on two isolated sections of line. These have since been linked, and through services can now be operated. Interesting features are the adoption of the broad Indian railway gauge of 1.676m (5ft 6ins), the use of unballasted track, and the operation of Indian-built rolling stock. The only other Indian metro is a short (5km) line in Madras, though a rapid transit system has recently been authorised in Delhi.

Above – Two views of the Shanghai metro, which features German-built rolling stock. *IRJ/SMC*

Below – Rolling stock for the troubled Taipei VAL line, where construction problems delayed the start of public services. *GEC Alsthom*

Mention has been made in an earlier chapter of the metro systems in operation in two cities of former Soviet Asia, namely Novosibirsk and Tashkent. Another is being built in Omsk. Other operational networks in Asiatic cities include elevated light rail systems in Manila and Taipei, and a fine modern metro in Singapore, to the construction of which many countries contributed; this system is being extended. Metros under construction in Asia include systems in Ankara, Bangkok, Izmir, Kaohsiung and Kuala Lumpur. The first section of the Kuala Lumpur light rapid transit system was opened in 1996. In Iran, work on a French-designed metro in Teheran was brought to a halt after the downfall of the Shah, but was resumed after a five-year delay. New metros are planned in several other Asiatic cities, notably Jakarta and Tel Aviv.

Singapore: a six-car train on an elevated section of the original line. *LTA, Singapore*

Turning now to Australia, we find two cities – Sydney and Melbourne – with important underground lines in the inner city areas. In neither case, however, do these lines constitute a genuine metro; they could more properly be described as in-town sections of the extensive outer-suburban railway systems of both cities. In Sydney, the so-called 'City Railway' is in the form of a loop which is linked with the suburban network at Central and Wynyard Stations; the loop is some 5.6km (3½ miles) long, with four of its six stations below ground level. It is now supplemented by an eight-station light monorail of Swiss design in central Sydney. In Melbourne, the spectacular underground railway loop around the central area consists of four separate tracks, each linked to a different group of pre-existing suburban railways. Each track is reversible, and is operated in a different direction in the morning and evening peak periods. The loop has had the effect of dispersing the city's workforce through a series of stations around the city centre, instead of concentrating it all at one station, Flinders Street. It has also overcome the operational problems caused at Flinders Street by the imbalance between the large number of trains coming from the eastern suburbs and the smaller number from the western suburbs. Other systems of transit interest in Australia include a guided bus line in operation in Adelaide and a proposed new spine tunnel line in central Brisbane.

As yet there is only one substantive metro in Africa. This is to be found in the continent's largest city, Cairo, and was formed by the construction of a link between the Helwan and El Marg suburban lines, running in tunnel along the heavily-used Sadat (Tahrir Square) – Mubarak (Ramses Square) Station corridor. This link, opened in 1987, carries heavy intra-city traffic. Cairo also has a line of the up-graded tramway type, and other urban lines are being built. Alexandria, too, has a light rail system (the Ramleh line).

Elsewhere in Africa, Tunis has a light rail transit system, and metros or light rail lines are being built or planned in Algiers, Casablanca and Johannesburg.

A train on the first Cairo metro line, formed by linking the Helwan and El Marg lines across the city centre.
GEC Alsthom

Facts and Figures

The systems included in these tables are operational metros as defined in Chapter 1 of the text. Unless otherwise stated in the footnotes, the table excludes in-town sections of main-line railways not primarily used for intra-city traffic, light railways not wholly segregated from other forms of transport, and some short lines of the people-mover type with limited patronage. Any gaps in the table indicate that the information was not available at the time of compilation (1996).

City	Operating Authority	Year Opened	Route Length	Track Gauge	Max. Grad.	Min. Radius of Curves
Amsterdam	GVB	1977	40km	1.435m	3.2%	300m
Athens	ISAP	1904 (b)	25.84km	1.435m	4%	160m
Atlanta	MARTA	1979	74km	1.435m	3%	230m
Baku	Baku Metro	1967	29km	1.524m	4%	300m
Baltimore	MMTA	1983	24.9km	1.435m	4%	224m
Barcelona	TMB	1924	76.4km	1.674m 1.435m	4.5%	92m
	FGC (c)	1954	44km	1.435m	4%	150m
Beijing	Beijing MTRC	1969	42km	1.435m	3%	250m
Belo Horizonte	CBTU	1986	18.14km	1.600m	3%	130m
Berlin	BVG	1902	164.7	1.435m	4%	74.8m
Bilbao	CTB	1995	26.5km (e)	1.000m		
Boston	MBTA	1901	125km (e)	1.435m	5%	122m
Brussels	STIB/(f) MIBV	1976	40.5km	1.435m	6.2%	100m
Bucharest	Metrorex RA	1979	57.2km	1.435m	3.5%	150m
Budapest	BKV	1896 (g)	31.7km	1.435m	4%	300m
Buenos Aires	Metrovias	1913	44.7km (e)	1.435m	4%	80m
Cairo	NAT	1987 (h)	42.5km	1.435m		
Calcutta	Metro Rail	1984	16.65km	1.676m	2%	300m
Caracas	Metro de Caracas	1983	41km	1.435m	3.5%	225m
Chiba	Chiba Urban Monorail	1988	13.5km	Suspended Monorail		
Chicago	CTA	1892	169km	1.435m	4%	27.4m
Cleveland	GCRTA (i)	1955	30.7km	1.435m	3.73%	182.5m
Detroit	DTC	1987	4.8km	1.435m		
Ekaterinburg	Ekat. Metro	1992	10.8km	1.524m	4%	400m
Erevan	Erevan Metro	1981	10.9km	1.524m	4%	250m
Frankfurt -am-Main	Stadtwerte Frankfurt	1968	56.2km	1.435m	4%	35m
Fukuoka	FMTB	1981	17.8km(k)	1.067m		
Genoa	AMT	1990	3.4km	1.435m	5.5%	40m
Glasgow	SPTE	1896	10.4km	1.220m	6.25%	201m
Hamburg	HHA	1912	101km	1.435m	5%	70m
Helsinki	HKL/HST	1982	16.9km	1.524m	3.5%	400m

No. of Stations	Power Supply	Current Collection	No. of Cars	Max. Car Length	Max. Car Width	Passengers p.a. (millions)
40	750v 600v	3 Rail Overhead	113 (a)	18.67m	3.0m	49
23	750v	3 Rail	227	17.0m	2.8m	85
36	750v	3 Rail	240	23.0m	3.2m	69.9
18	825v	3 Rail	167	19.21m	2.7m	160
14	700v	3 Rail	100	22.88m	3.11m	12.8
106	1500v 1200v	3 Rail and Overhead	488	16.5m	3.14m	262.8
	1200v	Overhead		19.0m	2.7m	46.4
29	750v	3 Rail	304		2.8m	491
11	3000v	Overhead	11 (d)	91.56m (d)	2.98m	13.1
167	780v	3 Rail	1616	16.05m	2.65m	450
23 (e)	1500v	Overhead	64	17.8m	2.8m	
84	600v	3 Rail & Overhead	678	21.3m	3.05m	150
51	900v	3 Rail	192	18.2m	2.7m	84.6
39	750v	3 Rail	496	18.6m	3.1m	256.7
41	750v /600v	3 Rail	562	19.36m	2.7m	395
63	1500v 1100v 550v	Overhead 3 Rail	482	17.0m	3.2m	195.8
33	1500v	Overhead	200	21.4m	2.9m	300
17	750v	3 Rail	144	19.5m	2.74m	30
35	750v	3 Rail	378	21.36m	3.05m	325
14	1500v	Contact Rail	34			15
145	600v	3 Rail	1230	14.63m	2.84m	144
18	600v	Overhead	60	21.3m	3.15m	5.6
13	600v	4 Rail (u)	12	12.7m	2.8m	2.5
9	825v	3 Rail	48	19.21m	2.7m	
9	825v	3 Rail	108	19.21m	2.7m	52.3
82	600v	Overhead	212 (j)	24.29m (j)	2.65m	92.6
20	1500v	Overhead	132			114.8
3	750v	Overhead	8	26.0m (j)	2.2m	3.5
15	600v	3 Rail	41	12.75m	2.34m	14.7
89	750v	3 Rail	903	30.0m (j)	2.56m	176
13	750v	3 Rail	84	22.1m	3.2m	37.1

City	Operating Authority	Year Opened	Route Length	Track Gauge	Max. Grad.	Min. Radius of Curves
Hong Kong	MTRC	1979	43.2km	1.435m	3.2%	300m
Istanbul	IUAS	1989	19km	1.435m	6%	50m
Jacksonville	JTA	1989	2km	Rubber-tyred		
Kharkov	Kharkov Metro	1984	27km	1.524m	4%	300m
Kiev	Kiev Metro	1960	43.2km	1.524m	4%	400m
Kitakyushu	KKT	1985	8.4km	Monorail	4%	80m
Kobe	KMTB	1977	22.7km	1.435m	2.9%	300m
	KNTC	1981	10.9km	Rubber-tyred	5.8%	30m
Kuala Lumpur	Star	1996	12.0km	1.435m		
Kyoto	KMTB	1981	11.1km	1.435m	3.2%	260m
Lille	Transpole	1983	28.5km	Rubber-tyred	7%	
Lima	AATE	1995 (x)	20.8km	1.435m		
Lisbon	ML	1959	19km	1.435m	4%	150m
London	LT(LUL)	1863	392km (k)	1.435m	3.3%	100m
	DLR	1987	22.6km	1.435m	6.25%	40m
Los Angeles	LACMTA (i)	1993	10.3km	1.435m	4%	274m
Lyon	TCL	1978	25.7km (l)	Rubber-tyred	20% (l)	80m (l)
Madras	Madras Metro	1991	5.0k	1.676m		
Madrid	Metro de Madrid	1919	118.5km	1.445m	5%	90m
Manila	LRTA	1984	14km	1.435m	0.4%	250m
Marseille	RTM	1978	19.5km	Rubber-tyred	7%	105m
Medellin	ETMVA	1995	28.8km	1.435m	3.7%	300m
Mexico City	STC Metro	1969	177.7km	Rubber-tyred (n)	6.8%	105m
Miami	Metro-Dade TA	1984	33km	1.435m	2%	305m
Milan	ATM	1964	68.7km	1.435m	3.5%	135m
Minsk	Minsk Metro	1984	18.58km	1.524m	4%	300m
Monterrey	Metrorey	1991	23.5km	1.435m		
Montreal	STCUM	1966	65km	Rubber-tyred	6.5%	140m
Moscow	Moscow Metro	1935	243.6km	1.524m	4%	196m
Munich	SWM	1971	66.8km	1.435m		
Nagoya	NMTB	1957	76.5m	1.435m 1.067m	3.5%	125m
Naples	FS	1993	9.5km	1.435m	5.5%	150m
Newcastle-upon-Tyne	Tyne & Wear PTE	1980	59.1km	1.435m	3.3%	210m
New York	NYCTA	1867	398km	1.435m		52m
	PATH	1908	22.2km	1.435m	4.8%	27.4m
	Staten Island RT		23km	1.435m	1.9%	152.4m
Nizhni Novgorod	N.N. Metro	1985	9.8km	1.524m	4%	400m
Novosibirsk	Novosibirsk Metro	1985	13km	1.524m	4%	400m

No. of Stations	Power Supply	Current Collection	No. of Cars	Max. Car Length	Max. Car Width	Passengers p.a. (millions)
38	1500v	Overhead	759	22.85m	3.1m	804
18	750v	Overhead	105 (j)	23.5m (j)	2.56m	36
4	750v	Side-beams		26.0m (j)	2.06m	
20	750v	3 Rail	171	19.21m	2.7m	250
36	825v	3 Rail	526	19.21m	2.7m	365
12	1500v	Monorail beam	36	60.47m (d)	2.98m	11.9
16	1500v	Overhead	168	19.0m	2.79m	95
15	600v	Siderail	112	8.4m	2.15m	29.5
13		3 Rail	34 (j)			
13	1500v	Overhead	102	20.0m	2.78m	75.8
39	750v	Side-beams	83 (j)	26.14m (j)	2.06m	49.8
	1500v	Overhead	60			
25	750v	3 Rail	142	16m	2.7m	136
245 (k)	600v	4 Rail	3992	18.37m	2.84m	784
32	750v	3 Rail	70 (j)	28m (j)	2.65m	15
8	750v	3 Rail	30	22.86m	3.2m	5
33	750v	Side-beams(m)	178	18m	2.89m	82.7
5	750v	3 Rail				
163	600v	Overhead	1048	18m	2.8m	413
18	750v	Overhead	64 (j)	29.28m (j)	2.5m	120
24	750v	Side-beams	144	16.19m	2.6m	54.7
25	1500v	Overhead	126	22.9m	3.2m	55
154	750v	Side-beams (n)	2541	16.7m	2.5m	1422.6
21	700v	3 Rail	136	22.86m	3.18m	14.5
83	750v 1500v	3 Rail Overhead	714	17.54m	2.85m	344.7
17	825v	3 Rail	132	19.21m	2.7m	149
21	1500v	Overhead	25 (j)			25
65	750v	Side-beams	759	17.2m	2.5m	197
150	825v	3 Rail	4060	19.21m	2.7m	3183.9
77	750v	3 Rail	474	18.0m	2.9m	284.3
84	600v 1500v	3 Rail Overhead	730	20.0m	2.8m	434.9
9	1500v	Overhead	12 (j)	35.68m (j)	2.85m	
46	1500v	Overhead	90 (j)	27.8m (j)	2.65m	39.5
469	625v	3 Rail	5803	22.86m	3.05m	1100
13	650v	3 Rail	342	15.6m	2.8m	59.2
22	600v	3 Rail	77	22.86m	3.05m	5.1
8	825v	3 Rail	36	19.21m	2.7m	66
10	825v	3 Rail	72	19.21m	2.7m	82

City	Operating Authority	Year Opened	Route Length	Track Gauge	Max. Grad.	Min. Radius of Curves
Nuremburg	VAG	1972	23.2km	1.435m	4%	100m
Osaka	OMTB	1933	105.8km	1.435m	3.5%	120m
	ICTS	1981	6.6km	Rubber-tyred		
	OKT	1990	6.7km	Monorail		
Oslo	Oslo Sporveier (o) (T.banen)	1966	49km	1.435m	5%	200m
Paris	RATP(q) (Metro)	1900	201.4km	1.435m	4%	40m
Philadelphia	SEPTA(i)	1908	41km	1.581m 1.435m	5%	32m
	PATCO	1969	23.3km	1.435m	5%	61m
Porto Alegre	Trensurb	1985	27.8km	1.600m		
Prague	DPMetro	1974	43.4km	1.435m	4%	350m
Pusan	PUTA	1985	32.5km	1.435m	3%	210m
Pyongyang	Pyongyang Metro	1973	22.5km	1.435m		
Recife	CBTU	1985	20.5km	1.600m	2%	312m
Rio de Janeiro	Metro de Rio de J(e)	1979	23km	1.600m	4%	500m
Rome	COTRAL	1955	33.5km	1.435m	4%	100m
Rotterdam	RET(a)	1968	72.9km	1.435m	3%	60m
Samara	Samara Metro	1987	12.5km	1.524m	4%	400m
San Francisco	BART(s)	1972	115km	1.676m	4%	120m
Santiago de Chile	Metro de Santiago	1975	27.3km	Rubber-tyred	4.8%	205m
São Paulo	Metro de São Paulo	1974	43.6km	1.600m	4%	300m
Sapporo	SCTB	1971	45.2km	Rubber-tyred	4.3%	200m
Sendai	SCTB	1987	14.8km	1.067m	3.5%	160m
Seoul	Seoul Metro Subway Corp.	1974	133km	1.435m	3.5%	400m
Shanghai	Shanghai Metro Corp.	1993/5 (t)	16.1km	1.435m	3.4%	300m
Singapore	SMRT	1987	83km	1.435m	3%	300m
Stockholm	SL	1950	110km	1.435m	4.8%	200m
St Petersburg	St P. Metro	1955	91.75km	1.524m	4%	400m
Taipei	TRTC	1996 (x)	10.9km	Rubber-tyred		
Tashkent	Tashkent Metro	1977	30km	1.524m	4%	400m
Tbilisi	Tbilisi Metro	1965	23km	1.524m	4%	400m
Tianjin	Tianjin Metro	1980	7.8km	1.435m	3%	300m
Tokyo	TRTA	1927	169.1km	1.435m 1.067m	4%	90m
	TBTMG	1960	68.1km	1.435m 1.372m 1.067m	3.5%	167m
	Yurikamome Line	1995	12km	Rubber-tyred		
	Tokyo Monorail	1964	16.9km	Monorail	6%	120m

No. of Stations	Power Supply	Current Collection	No. of Cars	Max. Car Length	Max. Car Width	Passengers p.a. (millions)
33	750v	3 Rail	150	18.8m	2.9m	81.7
99	750v 1500v	3 Rail Overhead	1086	18.9m	2.89m	988.6
8	600v	Sidebeams	72			22.5
5	1500v	Monorail beam	24			1.4
57	750v	3 Rail	217 (p)	36.6n (j)m	3.3m	52 (p)
372	750v	3 Rail(r)	3406	15.5m	2.4m	1170
62	625v	3 Rail	365	20.57m	3.07m	53.7
13	685v	3 Rail	121	20.57m	3.05m	11.2
15	3000v	Overhead	100	22.5m		38.6
46	750v	3 Rail	536	19.21m	2.71m	531
34	1500v	Overhead	300	18m	2.75m	195.7
17	825v	3 Rail	48	18.8m	2.7m	42
17	3000v	Overhead	100			40.7
25	750v	3 Rail	178	21.88m	3.17m	82.4
43	1500v	Overhead	378	17.84m	2.85m	208
41	750v	3 Rail & Overhead	142	28.6m (j)	2.68m	78
9	825v	3 Rail		19.21m	2.7m	
34	1000v	3 Rail	590	22.86m	3.2m	74
37	750v	Side-beams	250	16.79m	2.6m	167.1
41	750v	3 Rail	588	21.75m	3.17m	623.8
44	750v 1500v	3 Rail Overhead	400	18.0m	3.08m	234.9
17	1500v	Overhead	80	21.75m	2.88m	60.1
112	1500v	Overhead	1130	20m	3.18m	1354
13	1500v	Overhead	96	23.34m	3.0m	87
48	750v	3 Rail	510	23m	3.2m	256
100	650–750v	3 Rail	829	17.4m	2.8m	260 (e)
50	825v	3 Rail	1205	19.21m	2.7m	850
12	750v	Side-beams	102	26m (j)	2.06m	35
26	825v	3 Rail	146	19.21m	2.7m	180
20	825v	3 Rail	161	19.21m	2.7m	144
8	750v	3 Rail	18	19.52m	2.65m	10.5
154	600v 1500v	3 Rail Overhead	2401	20.0m	2.87m	2112.7
69	1500v	Overhead	632	20.0m	2.79m	595.6
12		3 Rail		8.5m	2.47m	
9	750v	Monorail beam	114	14.5m	3.02m	61

City	Operating Authority	Year Opened	Route Length	Track Gauge	Max. Grad.	Min. Radius of Curves
Toronto	TTC Metro	1954	60.8km	1.495m	3.45%	
	TTC-ALRT	1985	7km	1.435m	5.2%	18m
Toulouse	Semvat	1993	10km	Rubber-tyred	7%	150m
Valencia	FGV	1988 (v)	124km (c)	1.000m		
Vancouver	BC Transit Skytrain	1986	28.8km	1.435m	6%	18m
Vienna	Wiener Stadtwerke (w)	1976	38.5km	1.435m	4%	300m
Warsaw	Warsaw Metro	1995	11.2km	1.435m	3.1%	300m
Washington	WMATA	1976	144km	1.435m	4%	213m
Wuppertal	WSW	1901	13.3km	Suspended Monorail	4%	75m
Yokohama	YMTB	1972	33.0km	1.435m	3.5%	125m
	New Transit	1989	10.6km	Rubber-tyred	4%	50m

(a)   Including Sneltram
(b)   Date of opening after electrification
(c)   Excluding Catalans metre-gauge line operated by FGC
(d)   Multiple-car units
(e)   Including one light rail line
(f)   Excluding 'pre-metro' lines
(g)   Including Millennium line
(h)   First underground line
(i)   Excluding light rail lines
(j)   Articulated or permanently coupled units
(k)   Excluding sections of main-line railways over which metro trains also run
(l)   Including one line of rack railway
(m)   Excepting rack railway, which is steel-on-steel with overhead current collection
(n)   Excepting one line, which is steel-on-steel with overhead current collection
(o)   Excepting western light rail lines
(p)   Including western light rail lines
(q)   Excluding Regional Express system (RER), operated jointly by RATP and French Railways (SNCF)
(r)   Also through sidebeams of guideway on rubber-tyred lines
(s)   Excluding Muni ('Metro' light rail system)
(t)   Provisional opening 1993; full public service inaugurated in 1995
(u)   Linear induction system, with reaction rail
(v)   Opening of central in-town section
(w)   Excluding former Stadtbahn lines
(x)   Start of commercial operation delayed

No. of Stations	Power Supply	Current Collection	No. of Cars	Max. Car Length	Max. Car Width	Passengers p.a. (millions)
59	600v	3 Rail	546	22.7m	3.1m	158.7
6	600v	4 Rail (u)	28	12.7m	2.8m	12
15	750v	Side-beams	58	26.0m(j)	2.06m	50.8
	1500v	Overhead	168			19.2
20	600v	4 Rail (u)	150	12.7m	2.8m	20.1
54	750v	3 Rail	231	18.4m	2.8m	273
11	750v	3 Rail	42	19.2m	2.7m	35
74	750v	3 Rail	764	22.8m	3.04m	153.6
19	600v	Contact Rail	28(j)	24.06m	2.2m	23.6
27	750v	3 Rail	186	18m	2.78m	119.3
14	750v	Contact Rail	85	8m	2.38m	14

Index